WITH WINGS
ON THEIR
FINGERS

An Intimate View of the Flying-fox

WITH WINGS ON THEIR FINGERS

An Intimate View of the Flying-fox

PAMELA CONDER

Angus&Robertson
An imprint of HarperCollinsPublishers

*This book was written with the support of the
1991 Thomas Ramsay Science and Humanities Fellowship
of the Museum of Victoria.*

*This book is dedicated to Lorrie Conder, my mother,
whose loving support and encouragement made it possible,
and to my brother Leigh for his unfailing willingness to help.*

An Angus & Robertson Publication
Angus&Robertson, an imprint of
HarperCollins*Publishers*
25 Ryde Road, Pymble, Sydney NSW 2073, Australia
31 View Road, Glenfield, Auckland 10, New Zealand
77–84 Fulham Palace Road, London W6 8JB, United Kingdom
10 East 53rd Street, New York NY 10022, USA

First published in Australia in 1994

National Library of Australia
Cataloguing-in-Publication data:
Conder, Pamela.
   The wing-footed ones.
   ISBN 0 207 18403 8
   Flying foxes. I. Title.
599.4

Cover illustration by Pamela Conder, from the private collection of J. McIntyre.

9 8 7 6 5 4 3 2 1
98 97 96 95 94

Contents

Acknowledgements

A great many people have contributed to this book in a multitude of ways: supporting me with encouragement, advice, information and in some cases simply the friendship and laughter that made it possible to keep going. Amongst those to whom I owe thanks are Dr John E. Nelson, who not only shared his extensive experience with bats, but read the manuscript and, along with Dr Alan Lill and Mrs Sue Swann endured my wailing and gnashing of teeth about the progress of this work over Friday cappuccino for several years — I am very grateful to all three of them for this.

My sincere thanks are also due to Dr Les Hall, Greg Richards, Assoc. Prof. Dr R. L. Hughes, Dr Len Martin, Dr Chris Tideman, Dr Rosemary Booth, Mrs Helen Luckhoff and Mrs Lorraine Jolly, who have shared their considerable expertise, patiently answered innumerable questions and advised on various parts of the manuscript.

Without the help of my brother, Leigh Conder, in computer related matters, this project would have taken twice as long to finish. Without the long-suffering performance of duties above and beyond the call of motherhood by Lorrie Conder, it might never have been finished at all.

Dr Gary Ades, Nancy and Ron Ashenden, Frau Altmann, Mr Imants Dizgalvis, Sue Earle, Dr Richard Faust, Paul Fox, Barbara and Graeme George, Simon Hicks and the people of the Jersey Wildlife Preservation Trust, especially Bryan Carroll, Janette Young and the bat team, Ms Daphne Hills and the Mammal Department, Natural History Museum, London, Dr Dieter Kock, Lindy Lumsden, Stuart Norrington, Jan McIntyre, Prof. Angus Martin, Prof. J. Pettigrew, Dr K. C. Searle, Ronald Strahan and Prof. James Warren have all assisted me in a multitude of ways, for which I am deeply grateful. The Science and Humanities Committee of the Museum of Victoria, Lindy Allen, Frank Coffa, Liza Dale, Dr T. Darragh, Joan Dixon, Lina Frigo, Richard Gillespie, Alan McEvey, Rodney Start, Elizabeth Thompson, the staff of the Museum of Victoria Library are but a few of the many at the Museum to whom I owe thanks.

I would also like to express my gratitude for the help and cooperation of the management and staff of Healesville Sanctuary, in particular Karen Garth and all those associated with the maintenance of the flying-foxes there. Inevitably there are many others, not mentioned here by name, but to whom I am no less grateful. My warm thanks also to Alison Pressley and Sandra Lanzoni of HarperCollins Publishers for their support and encouragement.

Introduction

There is a sense of exhilaration and privilege in being permitted by a group of animals to observe them in the intimate workings and rituals of their society. This was all I had originally asked or expected of this project. However, thanks to the suggestions, advice, goadings and other assistance provided by a number of people and organisations, the intended one-year study of flying-fox behaviour has burgeoned into several years of much wider ranging investigation, and this book.

By the time the project was entering its fourth year, the flying-foxes had more or less taken over my life and it became clear that things had reached a critical point. I could not paint exhibitions to support the bat study without arresting its progress. It was also becoming apparent that, for the book to fulfil its purpose, there was much more work to be done aside from behavioural observations.

To my great relief and gratitude, the impasse was resolved by the Science and Humanities Committee of the Museum of Victoria. I was awarded the 1991 Thomas Ramsay Science and Humanities Fellowship of the Museum of Victoria. This annual award is aimed at supporting projects in which science and aspects of the humanities combine to enhance one another. The concept is far-sighted and all too rare in a world where these two great streams of our culture are in danger of alienation from each other to the ultimate impoverishment of both.

Quite apart from the financial support this brought to the project, it opened up the magnificent resources of the Museum's collections and Natural Sciences Library, full of important historical material as well as current scientific publications, for me to expand my field of study beyond the book's original concept. This was further enhanced by the opportunity to draw on the advice and inspiration of staff, expert in a number of related disciplines. I am particularly grateful to Joan Dixon, Curator of Mammalogy, and her assistant Lina Frigo, who frequently found time, in the midst of their own work, to help me negotiate the maze of the collections or offer opinions and advice.

Throughout most of this book I have tried to simplify matters by referring to members of the genus *Pteropus* as flying-foxes and the rest of the Megachiroptera as fruit bats. Many authorities regard these common names as interchangeable. In fact, neither term is particularly desirable, as they have nothing to do with foxes and many species of Megachiroptera live predominantly on blossoms, pollen and nectar. In this country at least, the term fruit bat tends to reinforce unfortunate connotations with untoward activities in the nation's orchards. I continue to refer to them where necessary as 'bats', as the debate continues about their evolutionary affiliations.

Many of the grey-headed flying-foxes whose stories are told here can still be met in the Healesville Sanctuary. One of the most interesting aspects of becoming intimately acquainted with this colony over the years has been watching the enduring nature of associations between individuals, and the subtle changes in these relationships as they adapt to altered circumstances, such as maturation of young and the departure of dominant males. The 'personality' of each animal in the group also became clearly distinguishable over time — some nervous, some more aggressive, some, like Phil, 010's golden-blond son, remained quiet and gentle, even when subjected to the indignities of being tagged and stuffed into a bag for weighing. Some flying-foxes appear to be born screamers, both in their own social doings and at any humans taking liberties with them, whilst others seldom vocalise in the normal course of things.

The style of the paintings in this book is not intended as scientific or photorealist illustration. These are animals painted to convey a personal view, with the artist's eye tempering the naturalist's observation. I hope that they will share with the reader, should words fail to do so, some of the intense pleasure I derive from the society of *Pteropus* and other denizens of its world.

Pamela Conder
Healesville
March, 1994

CHAPTER 1

'TI' Time

Late in 1988 I returned from a trip to China, where I had been at an international mammalogists' meeting, and had then gone looking for evidence of bats in Chinese art and architecture. I was still in the throes of unpacking vile-smelling field gear and attempting to make sense of reams of scribbled notes when a phone call came from the University of Queensland: would I like to come along as artist, assistant bat-wrangler and dogsbody on a field trip to the Torres Strait Islands? I promptly threw my field gear into the wash then repacked it.

A few weeks later I landed on Horn Island in a shimmer of heat and pale dust. After a brief wait, sheltering from the sun in the bright stuffiness of the airstrip's tiny arrivals building, the passengers straggled into a vehicle to pound across the island to the waterfront, along a track lined with cycads, termite mounds, and eucalypts with strangely light, bright-green foliage. Thursday Island is the chief administration centre of the Torres Strait, lying about 30 kilometres north of Cape York. Those of us heading for 'TI', as it is known locally, boarded the launch that forms the second stage of the airport shuttle. We churned through clear, quiet waters, only slightly less deep turquoise than they had been from the air. From 3000 metres one has the impression of flying over a carpet of kingfisher feathers, dotted here and there with islands, like chips of malachite dropped into spills of pallid gold dust.

The organisers of the project were Dr Les Hall from the University of Queensland, and Greg Richards from the CSIRO, both eminent 'bat men' who were already familiar with the islands. On a previous trip they had caught the first specimens of an undescribed flying-fox — soon to be known as the Torresian flying-fox. They were being joined on this trip by Dr Leon Hughes, also a denizen of the University of Queensland, who would act as consultant. One objective was, of course, to catch more of the new flying-foxes for study. The primary concern, however, was to examine the feasibility of setting up a training scheme for the islanders, so that regular sampling for rabies and screwworm could be carried out on island flying-fox populations. This being the most likely route of entry to mainland Australia, regular monitoring could avert a potentially ruinous situation.

For the time being, I had more pressing matters on my mind. Through the mid-morning heat shimmer I could see two pubs — one a fairly long walk around the beach front, the other closer, but up a steepish hill. Rather than hazarding a guess at which of them was expedition headquarters, I dawdled on the pier, squinting between the planks at water stiff with small fish darting back and forth past the lines dangled by unconcerned anglers. As I drifted pleasantly into that time zone peculiar to islands such as this, familiar figures came loping along the beach road. Les and Greg had not expected the flight to come from Cairns until late afternoon. Nevertheless, happening to recognise a distant green hat from the balcony of the Federal Hotel, where they had been

Female Torresian flying-fox.

reclining for 'a bit of a think', they decided to see who was under the hat. Scientific curiosity can be a wonderful thing.

Duly retrieved for higher purposes than sitting in the sun and contemplating sardines, I joined the others in the business of organisation. There were arrangements to be made with the Department of Primary Industry (DPI) and we strolled around for a chat with Lionel Smith, its chief on 'TI', who happened to be castrating a cat at the time. He finished up and we sat around drinking tea under the operating table fan, the cat's disembodied testes gleaming like small pink pearls beside their erstwhile owner while he slept off the anaesthetic. The DPI runs an efficient neutering service for domestic pets in the islands to avoid the problem of unwanted animals becoming feral. The walls were papered with snapshots and press cuttings referring to the DPI's multifarious activities — seizure of vessels loaded with Rusa deer antlers, a highly illegal bagful of live crocodiles, crocodile skins and New Guinean spotted cuscuses, amongst other things. Not far from the office, Indonesian fishing vessels bobbed in the harbour, impounded for illegal entry into Australian Territorial Waters.

Our flurry of organisational activity was punctuated by lunch, taken while sheltering from a tropical downpour under the verandah of Geraldine's Rainbow Motel on 'TI's main drag. As we struggled with vast constructions of beef, egg, salad and whatever else could be crammed between buns, a van pulled up in front of us. The legend adorning its panelwork advertised the owner's stock in trade — 'Plumbing, Pipe-laying, Drainage, Effluent Disposal and Funeral Director' — almost caused us to choke on our last decent meal for some time.

Later that day, a boat trip back to Horn, followed by 15 minutes in a light aircraft, brought Les, Greg, Leon and me to the Moa Island airstrip. The tiny aircraft touched down on a strip barely discernible in the rain-softened red earth, disgorged us amongst a tangle of equipment and purred swiftly away in preparation for take-off. As the engine noise receded it was replaced by the roar of a four-wheel drive, as a local storekeeper from Kubin village screeched to a halt beside us. His passengers — two young women and a boy — spilled from the cabin, before the driver tore off in pursuit of the aircraft. They were to fly to a church festival on Saibai. Since the days of the London Missionary Society, the church has been a central element in the life of these islands.

Nearby, in the hot shadow of a metal awning attached to a doorless tin shed, was a lone, still figure enthroned on an Esky. He stared dispiritedly into the glaring sky. As we approached, 'Kelvin' arose and welcomed us laconically to the Moa Airport passenger lounge. He had been there for some hours, waiting for the aircraft scheduled to collect him and his Esky full of crayfish 'for the boss' early that morning. We also waited, perched on a couple of old saw horses, in the quietly blistering heat. Our arrangements, it seemed, had gone amiss due to a funeral in St Pauls village.

Eventually Willem Pedro, a man whose great charm matched his stature, rolled up to the 'lounge' in the St Pauls church's new four-wheel drive. He was the DPI 'co-operator' for the area, responsible for registering pigs and other livestock, monitoring the sterilisation of dogs and cats and watching the activities of yachts and other craft in the area. The need for the four-wheel drive became bone-gratingly obvious as we bounced for an hour over creek beds and along a track which changed its course around the trees according to the latest rain damage.

The light had taken on a near-evening gentleness by the time we reached St Pauls village on the eastern side of Moa Island. St Pauls was originally a South Sea Islander reserve under control of a Government Resident based on Thursday Island. The people had come from nearby Mabuiag Island after problems arose between the South Sea Islanders and the Mabuiag people around the turn of the century. The village was originally known as Wag, but was renamed after the people requested that a Christian teacher be appointed for their children and the settlement became a part of the Diocese of Carpentaria. The present-day population is about 100 people.

On arrival we were installed in the attractively sprawling house known, appropriately for our purposes, as 'the Ark'. It is the Bishop of Carpentaria's official residence in St Pauls, but doubles as guest accommodation. The Ark had been the bat base on Les and Greg's previous visits, so they introduced Leon and me to the idiosyncrasies of the plumbing, cooking equipment and resident wildlife. The most important warning was not to linger too long enjoying the ambience of the galvanised iron and concrete toilet on windy days. A large hole in the fibro roof bore mute witness to the destructive potential of a coconut dropping from the palm towering alongside.

The men graciously allotted me the bishop's bedroom, with the proper bed. They had not been fantasising — as I had suspected — with their description of the unusually civilised nature of this trip, even including a four-poster bed. There was no denying the fact that the bed had posts — about 2 metres of two-by-four nailed to each corner! In nights to come I lay in it, contemplating their chivalry, stifling in air redolent with the odour that only a mature male flying-fox in a confined area can produce emanating from bags of newly captured bats swinging gently from the beam across the door. The bedroom windows were, for some unfathomable reason, firmly nailed shut.

The first captures were made on the evening we arrived — not flying-foxes, but two species of microbats. The bats of the world fall into two basic categories or suborders, Microchiroptera and Megachiroptera. Together they make up the order

Chiroptera, meaning 'hand-winged ones'. Although the micros are often thought of as being insectivorous, some are, in fact, fruit or nectar feeders, some hunt prey such as frogs or fish, and a couple live on blood. However, the majority of them echolocate, have poor vision, and are active at night. The megabats, on the other hand, are nectar, blossom and fruit eaters. They have well-developed eyes, specially adapted for low-light vision, and an excellent sense of smell. Other than those belonging to the genus *Rousettus*, they do not echolocate, but more about that later. In spite of the encompassing terms 'mega' and 'micro', the largest micros are far larger than the smallest megas. Compare, for instance, the ghost bat (*Macroderma gigas*), a micro, with the tiny megachiropteran northern blossom bat (*Macroglossus minimus*), both Australian species.

As the afternoon light dimmed rapidly, the first task was to set up the bat-catching nets and harp trap. Heavy gauge nets were set on aluminium poles near some fruiting beach almond trees (*Terminalia catappa*), favoured as a food source by flying-foxes. The finer net and a harp trap were set up amongst the mango trees, bombax, bush passionfruit and tangled scrub in a spot we came to know, from painful experience, as Green Ant Creek. These were for the smaller tube-nosed (*Nyctimene robinsoni*) and northern blossom bats (*Macroglossus minimus*). The net would be checked repeatedly throughout each night and rolled up at five-thirty each morning, before birds were in flight and susceptible to entanglement.

The work now underway, Les and Greg quietly disappeared into the St Pauls church, just across the sandy track from the Ark. Perhaps in search of spiritual nourishment as insurance against the dinner of bully beef and tomato sauce awaiting us, I surmised. Whatever they were looking for, they soon reappeared brandishing well-filled bat bags. From one emerged a male sheath-tailed bat (*Taphozous australis*) and from the others, two female long-eared bats (*Nyctophilus bifax*) with young clinging to the nipples and fur beneath their wings like minuscule bombs. When the one carrying twins was weighed, we found that the combined weight of the babies precisely equalled that of the mother. In the course of collecting forearm measurements and other data, the mother of the single youngster managed to escape and depart through the open louvre window, leaving us with her 5-gram offspring.

The business of hand-rearing insectivorous bats is not easy at the best of times and this little one's prospects looked decidedly dim. The babies are born naked and take a week or so to become properly furred. This one was probably three to four weeks old, which meant it was between two and three weeks away from flying independently. However, on the off chance of a rescue, it was taken back to the church with the others. As Les, carrying the bag, approached the door, he was dive-bombed by a tiny black shadow — the baby's mother. As soon as her young was

Sheath-tailed bat (*Taphozous australis*).

extracted from the bag and hung on the notice board, she swooped and disappeared into the evening with it.

Darkness was close by the time we could relax and begin to 'feel' the island. We walked along the eggshell-white beach, watching a Turneresque sunset. Light bounced off an opalescent sea beyond the reef, turning rocks and mangroves to soft rich gold. Small bats scooted through still air, and skinks, their heavy bodies striped with reddish-orange, trailed long, thin tails through the pumice pebbles. We sat on a driftwood log, talking quietly of watercolour skies, listening to geckos chuckling in the trees behind us. I wondered privately why the thought of capturing on paper or canvas the opulent composition of colour and form all around made me shudder. The idea of art attempting to imitate nature often seems vaguely obscene in its arrogance. But perhaps we all have the instinct to somehow appropriate transient beauty for our own — to take it with us.

In the nets around the beach almond trees we caught the most important quarry — the flying-foxes: the large black flying-fox (*Pteropus alecto*), which is also found on the mainland, and a small black flying-fox with a striking ruff of auburn fur behind the head. The latter is known to science only since Les and Greg discovered it in the beach almonds around the Ark on an earlier trip. If capture offended the bats' dignity, it certainly did not affect their appetites. They gulped down tinned fruit and syrup, stuffing their cheek pouches until the taut, glossy black skin looked like bags of marbles.

The island children, on holiday from school, were keen to join in the bat-catching. At times we would be surrounded by a retinue of 20 madly enthusiastic assistants as we trudged around by moonlight checking nets. They offered encouragement in the form of regaling us with traditional island recipes for sautéed *sappur* (as the big bats are known on Moa). Our interest became less academic with every meal of gelatinous, sun-warmed beef and biscuits we choked down. We did, however, learn that the flying-foxes also have a traditional medical application: the fat is rendered down and rubbed on the legs of sufferers of coughs and other respiratory complaints.

At first, only the boys came to inspect the latest captures or take turns in wearing the headlamps on the nocturnal forays. But, seeing a woman in the group, some of the girls soon summoned the confidence to join in. Although the boys were clearly dominant, on at least one occasion some subtle feminine influence prevailed. In the heat of the afternoon we retreated into the Ark, where it was possible to work at the huge dining table, cooled by the trade winds blowing gently through the open louvres. Directly outside the windows, a lesser Lewin honeyeater and some glittering yellow-breasted sunbirds flittered in and out of the foliage. At the other end of the cavernous, high-ceilinged white room, I sat with a small group of girls, talking quietly about life on Moa. There is a gentleness and natural civility about the island children that seems to reflect the love and generosity of their family lives. Older children looked out for the smaller ones, not as a chore, but as part of the natural order of things. When things were to be shared, like the wearing of headlamps, rather than the expected competitive scuffle, there was lively concern that no one should miss his or her turn.

As the girls began to draw pictures in my sketchbook, the better to explain various traditions, some of the boys drifted from the table where they were watching the bat-work. Soon the pencil was being handed around as various ones were nominated as the experts on musical instruments, masks and so forth. In spite of the deep-rooted Christian spirit prevailing in the community, there is also obvious pride in the islanders' cultural heritage and legends.

We also learned more of the animal life on the island, listening to the children. The boys' dark eyes sparkled with excitement as they described the latest pig hunt. As usual, they had gone out with their dogs to find a sounder of wild pigs, the strategy being to let the dogs chase the adults and keep them busy while the boys hurtle after the piglets (which are taken home and raised). As sometimes happens, the method ran foul and the old boar failed to be taken in by the ruse. A boy was treed, but fell when his perch gave way and had his leg ripped open by the pig.

A chance remark from another youngster set us back on our heels. We had for some time had a running joke about the 'mythical Moan echidna', confident that no such beast existed. It is the sort of fantasy apt to seize mammalogists set out on unsurveyed islands, particularly after a few tins of bully beef. In the midst of a discussion as to who had what amongst their treasures, such as dugong teeth and pieces of turtle shell, one boy casually offered us some echidna spines he had found in the scrub!

Between six-thirty and seven in the evenings we would wander out into the cooling air and walk quietly along the powdery tracks, listening to the coucals and frogs calling from the tall grass. This was the time to raise the nets. An hour or so later, the Green Ant Creek net began yielding tube-nosed and blossom bats.

Blossom bats are nectar feeders and important pollinators. Their feeding habits are reflected in the structure of the slender conical head. The tongue is even longer than the head and covered with papillae (small projections), ideally suited to

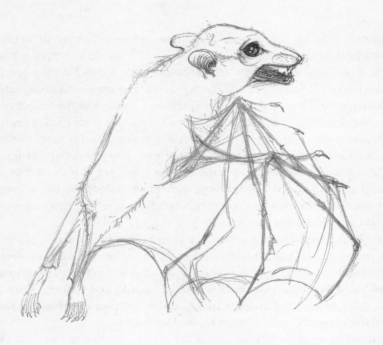

Northern blossom bat (*Macroglossus lagochilus*).

probing the depths of flowers to withdraw nourishment. The teeth are narrow and delicate, as might be expected. In common with the little red flying-fox (*Pteropus scapulatus*), also a nectivorous species, their dental arrangements often show abnormalities in the form of missing or additional teeth.

The tube-noses are spectacular little animals, weighing between 30 and 50 grams, with nostril structures protruding about 5 millimetres from the muzzle. Their wings and ears are splashed with yellow blotches, that, against the golden brown background, give them the appearance of desiccated leaves when they hang enfolded from a branch.

Many microchiropterans also have weirdly convoluted facial ornamentations and nose leaves, but in some cases these are thought to relate to one of the fundamental differences between them and the megabats: echolocation, or acoustic orientation. When bats vocalise, using low frequency sounds below 20 kilohertz, the sounds are audible to most of us. However, once the sound frequency moves above 20 kilohertz it is for the most part beyond the range of human hearing. These high-frequency calls are the ones commonly used by microbats, not only to navigate, but to locate food. One group of megabats, belonging to the genus

Rousettus, uses a form of echolocation to negotiate the flight paths of the dark roosts it favours. But this is an audible 'clicking' sound produced by the tongue, different to the inaudible ultrasonics produced in the larynx (voice box) of the microchiropterans. Although there is much still to be explained, the external nasal structures of some micros assist in beaming and directing the sound.

Tube-nosed bat (*Nyctimene robinsoni*).

To return to the *Nyctimenes,* they, like other megabats, rely on well-developed vision rather than echolocation to get about. They also have a well-developed sense of smell, far more useful than sonar in locating the blossoms and fruit they feed on. The arrangement of their teeth is particularly interesting. Instead of the usual arrangement of incisors, the front of the lower jaw is occupied by two canine teeth positioned so that they almost touch each other. These teeth meet with the two upper incisors when the bat closes its jaws. This peculiarity could assist the bat in piercing the tough skin of the fruit it eats. They are certainly effective little biters, if you happen to offer an annoyed specimen a finger.

The larger flying-foxes also have dentition capable of doing a fairly nasty job on a finger. In fact, they proved to be one of the very few things I have seen wipe the smile off Greg's face. The late evening net check was being carried out with an even more than usually zealous party of helpers wielding the flashlights. The excitement of seeing a very large and unamused *sappur* resisting arrest in the net caused lights to flash in all directions, trying to assist Greg as he manfully attempted to wrestle the beast free of its entanglement. Unfortunately, most of the beams were streaking across his eyes, rather than onto the bat, momentarily blinding him. The animal, seizing the initiative, performed a flurry of elegant slashes that would have done Errol Flynn credit, opening the Richards digits almost to the bone in several places.

Perhaps it was the effort of suppressing unparliamentary language in the

Tube-nosed bat (*Nyctimene robinsoni*).

presence of children that affected his usual effervescence when he arrived, white-faced and dripping blood, back at the Ark. His all-encompassing enthusiasm was briefly reignited by the news that I had some liquid Betadine in my kit — but soon extinguished by a few drops of it poured onto his wounds! I resisted the temptation to quote chapter and verse of *Bats of Eastern Australia*, one of my favourite bat references, written by none other than Hall and Richards: 'Bats must be held firmly, but not so as to cause stress or enough discomfort to cause them to bite.'

When they happen not to have their mouths full of bat worker, the flying-foxes use their impressive teeth to chew up fruits, which form part of their diet along with blossoms, nectar and pollen, in order to swallow the juice and spit out the fibrous material. This habit gave rise to the popular myth in Australia and India (and probably elsewhere too) that flying-foxes lack an anus and instead defecate through the mouth. I suppose the contributing logic being that for habitually upside-down animals, the conventional arrangement would result in fouled fur. However, flying-foxes, being well-organised animals, turn head up and hang by their thumbs when the need to urinate or defecate arises. The only ones fouled by this are those, like me, fool enough to wander around below without watching where they walk.

One important aim of the field trip was to find out more about the biology of the new species of flying-fox. So far, its known range did not extend much beyond the beach almond trees not far from the Ark, so finding the location of its day roost was the obvious place to start.

This time working with safely sedated *sappurs* laid out on the dining table, one black flying-fox (*Pteropus alecto*) and one of the new ones were fitted with radio transmitters. These were powered by small lithium batteries and attached to collars made from hospital wrist bands that had been lined with sheepskin. Using a large portable aerial and a small portable receiver unit, we hoped to pick up the bleeps emitted by the transmitters and track the bats to their roosts.

That evening our untiring troop of helpers had been invited to watch the release of the collared bats. Anxious to get on with the action, the first contingent arrived at the door before we had finished dinner. As we dithered over coffee, more boys arrived, screaming with excitement that 'a big *sappur*' was in the nearest net. We all tumbled out of the Ark, anxious to get the brute in hand before it fought its way out, as one had done the night before. *Pteropus alecto* is no sissy when it comes to dealing with mist nets. By the time we arrived with a bat bag, all we had was indigestion — the bat was long gone.

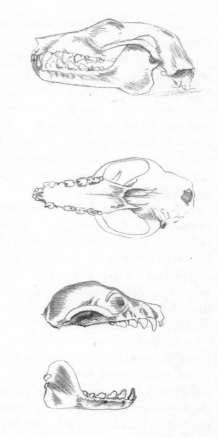

The skulls of the adult *(top)* and sub-adult black flying-fox (*Pteropus alecto*).

For the rest of the evening Les had a human hat. The smallest of the boys had been so terrified by the great black *sappur* that the rest of the net checks were carried out with him safely perched on Les's shoulders, legs firmly knotted around his neck and arms wrapped tightly around his forehead. Les simply trudged along, his usual beatific smile occasionally turning to a grimace when his air supply was reduced in direct proportion to the proximity of a bat-bearing net.

Eventually both collared bats were released and we repaired to the Ark to recover; however, not for long. The unmistakable noise of pteropids squabbling drifted through the louvres, so back out we went with the spotlight. As if mocking our efforts, two flying-foxes of the new species cackled as they licked the inflorescences high up in the palm behind the house. Not much later, a check with the receiver picked up the signal of the black flying-fox, but nothing was heard from the other.

The next day was Monday and our time on Moa was running out. In order to get a radio fix on the flying-foxes' roosts, Les and Greg decided we should head for high ground. First, however, we made an early morning visit to the store, where excitement almost won out over dignity at the sight of biscuits, cakes and cashew nuts after three days of bully beef and tinned vegies. If we were going on a forced march, it was not going to be without suitable fortification. High above the counter hung a blackboard advertising petrol and 'gene oil', which, we later learned, was not a lubricant for some genetic engineering project as we had speculated, but the local term for engine oil.

Our guide for the day was young George Nawie, who skipped and bounded through the tall bladey grass, up and down hills and across broken granite, clad only in a pair of shorts. We struggled in his wake, burning through our sunscreen and hats, tottering in our sturdy footwear. Crossing ridges and valleys, we at last stopped on the spur of Met Hill. From this vantage point we should have been able to get a clear signal from the sweep of land beneath us. Behind us stretched the sea, dotted with islets — perhaps one of these was the refuge the bats sought in daylight. But the receiver told us nothing.

We trekked on, descending a steep slope covered in loose rock and then through grassland, our mood enlivened briefly by Leon attempting a solo on a conch shell found along the way. It somehow lacked the mellifluous note of the French horn he was well known for his habit of practising up and down the corridors of the anatomy department in the dead of night! At midday we crossed a small area of level ground and found ourselves amongst the mangroves at the shoreline.

There was still no signal from the flying-foxes. Keeping a weather eye out for crocodiles, we collapsed thankfully in the shade, sitting on rocks and roots, with shallow water sparkling between the pebbles at our feet. The billy was soon boiling for our elegant picnic of instant noodles, apples and fruitcake. I thought it rather touching, the way Les meticulously extracted all the red imitation cherries from his cake and passed them over to Greg, that is until I learned that Les is rather finicky about ingesting anything he suspects of harbouring carcinogens, while Greg, being a smoker, regards them as insignificant in terms of added risk. The finale to the meal was lemon tea, swilled from the greasy noodle containers — and it tasted wonderful!

In no great hurry to desert this delightful spot, we each relaxed in our own way after the meal: Les waded out to a flat rock for a siesta, Greg smoked contentedly in the shade and I communed with a grey-green crab popping in out of a crevice between the stones at my feet. It was a particularly smart-looking animal, with its bright red racing trim edging its legs and claws. Leon and George wandered off to collect 'happy stones' from a nearby beach.

The idea of happy stones originated on York Island. One collects a stone of substantial size — the bigger the rock the greater the happiness — and endows it with a pleasant memory. The stone is then placed in a doorway, so that every time one passes through the door, that happy event will be invoked and one's mood elevated by the thought.

All too soon we had to gather our bits and pieces for the return to St Pauls and the business of putting up nets for the night. This time we walked along a relatively flat track through open grassland littered with 2- and 3-metre-high termite mounds and small kopjes of granite. Along the way George pointed out and identified the tracks of various birds, pigs and other denizens of Moa.

In our next attempt to track the radio-collared bats, we took to the sea. Early morning found us punctually lined up on the beach with a couple of drums of petrol, waiting for a boat in which to put them. Eventually, Sam Kris skipped his dinghy inside the reef — somewhat late, but the islands have their own time zone, '"TI" Time'. The philosophy is, 'Why do today what you can put off until you feel more like it?'. Very sensible too, once one shakes off the Great Southern Obsession.

First we crossed the reef and headed out to sea to Sam's island. Like most of the islanders, Sam is an expert seaman. At an age when many children down south can barely swim, the island youngsters are casually negotiating reefs with consummate skill, in search of the best spots to spear fish. A brief burst of pips from the receiver raised our hopes, but it soon fell silent again and remained obstinately mute for the rest of the trip. Perhaps a thump as we sped across the water dealt it a mortal blow.

About 40 minutes later we landed on Iem, Sam's garden island. He and his wife find it practical to make the trip to the island several times a week, to cultivate their crops of yams, cassava and wild gooseberries, rather than compete with the wild pigs on Moa. The dung from the generations of Torres Strait pigeons that roost on Iem makes its soil rich and fertile. Les and Greg speculated on the possibility that the bats were operating a sort of time-share arrangement with the pigeons, using the roost during the day while the pigeons were away feeding on Moa or elsewhere. At night the position would be reversed. This would be safer for the bats than roosting on Moa, where they could be hunted. This was not so far-fetched. In some areas, like Chillagoe in northern Queensland, insectivorous bats and swiftlets occupy the cave roosts in shifts. It is a spectacular sight at dusk to see the small bats shoot from the open top of a limestone karst tower and, moments later, the dark forms of tiny swiftlets dive unhesitatingly into the pitch-black hole.

Attractive as the idea was, we could find no sign of bats in pigeon roosts on Iem, so we returned to the dinghy to head for Moa Peak where we hoped to pick up the signal. We were fortunate to have Sam's help, for he was the only one who could guide us to Hotel Cave to search for smaller bats. The cave was named by Sam and his father, Barna Kris, many years ago when the family garden was located nearby. The evidence showed that it was a much-frequented and favoured haunt of wild pigs.

From the beach below Moa Peak we began another march through inhospitable bladey grass. This time the discomfort was ameliorated by the sight of brilliant magenta Cape York lilies, members of the ginger family. Their intense colour glowed against the taupe-coloured dust in small clearings. As we progressed inland, Sam stooped to fiddle around in the grass for a moment, then moved on. We thought he was hiding his cigarettes in a safe spot until he did it again and we looked back to see smoke rising behind us; he was taking the opportunity to burn off some grass, to promote regrowth.

Soon we entered the rainforest on the lower slopes, Sam slashing enthusiastically with his formidable bush knife to clear the path. I quietly wondered whether Moan rainforest would burn faster than we could run uphill. There were frequent halts as Sam pointed out plants and other wildlife, or gave impromptu lessons in bushcraft. In an area where the vegetation thinned slightly and crow's nest ferns sprouted from crevices in huge granite boulders, a scrub fowl, or megapode, dashed away. We stopped and sat quietly, while Les scrabbled in the debris on the forest floor, doing a creditable impersonation of a scrub fowl. The bird obviously thought so too, and returned to investigate the sounds, allowing us to see its rich, dark plumage with flashes of iridescence. It is a relative of the Australian brush turkey and also incubates its eggs in a mound, scratched together with its large, powerful feet.

The slope steepened and we scrambled over a rock fall to higher ground. In front of me, not much below eye level, I saw a slender, elegant snake gliding through a crevice between the rocks Leon was negotiating. My delighted exclamation, 'Look, there's a lovely snake just under you!', nearly caused him to lose his footing. I should perhaps have mentioned that it was a harmless green tree snake, which was in any case heading for the hills to escape us!

In the end, I did not actually set eyes on the 'hotel'. We split up to search for it and when I heard shots ring out higher up the peak, I assumed Sam was securing a few pork chops for lunch and thought it wiser not to get into the firing line – his or the pig's. In fact, the shots and the shouting, which I hoped did not indicate that one of the others had been taken for a swine, were to call us together at the cave. I was sweatily pursuing specimens of a long-tailed, tree-dwelling skink in the hope of contributing a new species to science, when the others reappeared with large grins and their shirts full of micro-chiropterans. The cave was well populated with fawn horse-shoe bats (*Hipposideros cervinus*).

In the early afternoon we descended, travelling faster this time in order to catch the tide. Back on the beach Sam's son waited patiently with the dinghy. Another half hour on the water saw us back on the beach at St Pauls.

Although our initial attempt at radio-tracking had failed to locate the new species' roost site, the colony was eventually discovered in the north of Moa when Les and Greg returned to the island.

Next day we again waited at Moa airstrip, watching Caspian terns and others gliding on elegantly pointed wings over shallow waterholes shimmering with an assortment of waders. There were curlews, spur-winged plovers, busy-looking dotterels

Horseshoe bat (*Hipposideros cervinus*).

scuttling about amongst the whimbrels and pied stilts. A grebe bobbed silently on the shining beige surface. Red haematite pebbles seemed to glow with the heat, as we waited for well over three hours.

One of the islanders, who had come to pick up passengers from another flight, kindly drove to Kubin village to call the airline for us. The message was relayed back to us that 'it wouldn't be long'. As Les commented acidly, they were right, it was not long — in geological time. Eventually we were collected, along with our rather odoriferous collection of bats, much to the pilot's disgust.

Being the smallest passenger is unwise when travelling in light aircraft. In keeping with loading recommendations the weight went to the front and the bats, the stench and I shared the tail end, bumping through the hot air back to Horn Island. But even that was part of the magic of a field trip in such a strange and wonderful part of the world.

CHAPTER 2

Is it a Bird, is it a Mouse?

CLASSIFYING FLYING-FOXES

On our return to Thursday Island, we made straight for the DPI with our cargo of three, by now thoroughly unamused, flying-foxes. There were two animals of the new species, as well as a youngish black flying-fox. Lionel very civilly invited them to make themselves at home in an old trap cage for the weekend. As Greg released them into the cage and I tossed in beach almonds for them to feed on, the male appeared torn between greed and bloodlust, attempting to simultaneously stuff his mouth with fruit and fasten his jaws onto the long-suffering Greg's digits. However, these remarkably adaptable creatures settled so rapidly into their new situation that less than 48 hours later they allowed me to reach into the cage and readily took fruit from my hand.

During the next couple of days there was time, at last, to observe the new flying-foxes at leisure, as I cleaned the cage, fed and drew them. I began to speculate on the matter of classifying animals, looking for the differences between the outwardly similar species. These specimens would help confirm the existence of the Torresian flying-fox as a species, adding evidence to that gathered from Les and Greg's first specimens. It remained for the scientific description and specific name to be accepted and published.

The naming of a species can be based on a number of things. It may make reference to a characteristic of the animal, its place of origin, or the name of a person, in Latin or Latinised form. (I have even heard of recently unearthed dinosaurs being christened in honour of the corporation which sponsored the work on their fossil remains.) *Pteropus*, a Latinised version of the Greek 'wing-footed', is the generic name for the flying-foxes and the specific name of Torresian flying-fox will honour Barna Kris, an elder of Moa Island and the father of Sam Kris.

Sam had told us of his father — more than 100 years old and living in a nursing home on 'TI' — as we toiled up Moa Peak. The surrounding area had

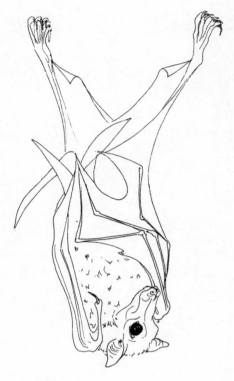

Torresian flying-fox.

been the site of the family garden during Sam's boyhood. They had lived there, working in the garden six days a week and walking to St Pauls village to church on Sundays. Sacks of produce or bananas were carried weekly over the peak or around it by way of the reefs. Barna Kris would distribute the food to those who needed it - never selling, simply sharing - a practice continued by Sam. He spoke proudly of his father's great strength. Sam recalled returning from a hunting trip when he was five years old, perched on one of his father's shoulders, on the other shoulder Barna Kris carried a wild pig. Who better to embody the spirit of Moa, in the name of its own flying-fox?

When an unfamiliar animal is found, like the flying-fox on Moa Island, one of the steps to discovering more about its biology is to investigate where it belongs in the scheme of things. 'Relatedness' can provide some guidelines to the study of an otherwise unknown species.

We can look for clues to the animal's lifestyle in its anatomical characteristics,

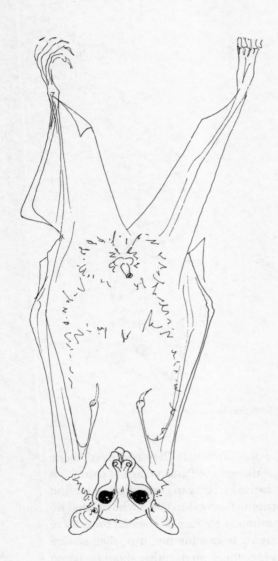

Male Torresian flying-fox.

as shown by Ogilby in 1892: *'Pteropus scapulatus*, Peters (1862) . . . In the length of the muzzle, and the very narrow unicuspidate teeth, this species differs so much from its congeners, and so closely resembles the long-tongued *Macroglossi*, as to make it probable that its food is similar to those forms.'

First of all, to establish whether it really is new to science, the literature must be searched for a description that could fit the specimen. The description of a species is a complex matter. To begin with, a 'shopping list' of known species is assembled and examined. Sometimes there is liaison with the British Museum, which holds a large collection of chiropteran *type specimens*. The *type*, or *holotype*, is the representative and supposedly typical animal from which the original description of the species was made. The idea of a typical individual is rather an arbitrary one. In view of the variations within some species, a group of specimens also used in the original diagnosis will be held along with the holotype. These are known as paratypes. (For those who wish to know more about zoological nomenclature, Ronald Strahan's *Dictionary of Australian Mammal Names*, Angus & Robertson, 1981, includes a concise summary of the terms and practices involved.)

In the case of the Torresian flying-fox, comparisons were made with all Pacific flying-foxes, regardless of size, then with all world species of similar size. Skins were prepared by Ian Mason of the CSIRO, one of the best preparators in Australia. The skulls were cleaned and measured for comparison of dimensions and characters with other species, for example, shape, size, proportions and teeth. Then comes number crunching on the computer. As it is so neatly put by Jepsen, 'Various intricate methods of dimensional and statistical analyses have been devised to express the differences in form of whole skeletons or parts of them.' (Jepsen, 1970.)

If the animal is unidentifiable through the scientific literature and museum collections, there are a number of things to be considered before it can be classified and 'christened'. It must also be established whether it merits the title of a 'full species' or a 'subspecies'. That is to say, to what degree do its characteristics differ from those of its closest known relative? In some cases this can remain a bone of contention amongst taxonomists, the scientists who specialise in the systematics, or classification of organisms.

The business of classification always reminds me of the Russian

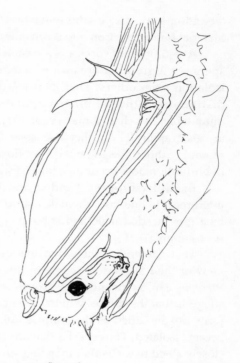

Torresian flying-fox.

babushka dolls, which open up, each containing all those smaller than itself. With the Torresian flying-fox, it is not too difficult to romp straight through to the level of genus, that is, it is obviously a bat, a member of the order Chiroptera, and it displays enough of the characteristics mentioned in the previous chapter to place it in the suborder Megachiroptera. Beyond that, a number of features, such as the skull and teeth, place it in the family Pteropodidae, subfamily Pteropodinae and the genus *Pteropus*.

The final step is to establish that the Torresian flying-fox's characteristics are sufficient to distinguish it completely from the 65 or so known species belonging to the genus *Pteropus*, many of which appear, superficially, quite similar to each other. This was brought home to me recently, as I sat for days amongst the extensive collections of assorted members of *Pteropus* at Frankfurt's Senckenberg Museum and the Natural History Museum in London, measuring and photographing skulls and examining skins. I was actually in pursuit of the mysterious dusky flying-fox, *Pteropus brunneus*, but at the same time keeping a weather eye out for anything that resembled the Torresian. As one whose defeatist view of systematics has long been 'abandon hope all ye who enter here', I was at last seduced by this wealth of material for comparison into reconsidering the matter of speciation.

A definition of species is a somewhat arbitrary matter. It could be said that a species is a group of organisms breeding (or potentially reproducing) in genetic isolation from others. That is, the group of individuals shares a pool of genes distinct from that of other populations of related animals. Species are not immutable, but change may occur very slowly when populations within a species are geographically or otherwise isolated. Generally speaking, genes can be passed around within a species, but do not flow back and forth between species. However, hybridisation does occur on a limited scale.

In captivity, grey-headed and black flying-foxes have been known to interbreed. In one case, a female hybrid of these two species was successfully mated by a grey-headed male and subsequently produced a male youngster. (L. Martin pers. comm., 1994.)

That a hybrid of these two species should be fertile is of particular interest in view of their supposed degree of 'un-relatedness'. The species within the genus *Pteropus* can be arranged in groups on the basis of shared characteristics. This suggests that the species within each group have a common origin from which their form was modified as the animals invaded new territories and some populations became isolated. Thus species that are geographically close are not necessarily more closely allied to each other than they are to a geographically distant one.

According to Andersen's Catalogue of Chiroptera (British Museum, 1912), the black flying-fox, *Pteropus alecto gouldii* (formerly known as *Pteropus gouldi*), is allied to *P. alecto* of Lombok, Sulawesi and Salayer; the spectacled flying-fox, *P. conspicillatus*, also occurs in southeastern New Guinea, and is closely related to species found in western New Guinea and the Moluccas; the little red flying-fox, *P. scapulatus*, is most closely related to *P. woodfordi* in the Solomon Islands, and the grey-headed flying-fox, *P. poliocephalus*, belongs to the *P. macrotis* group from New Guinea and the Aru Islands. Andersen suggests that, 'as *P. scapulatus* and *P. poliocephalus* are decidedly the most peculiarly modified' of the Australian species, they have perhaps occupied the continent longer than the others. Interestingly, Andersen accepts *P. brunneus*, the dusky flying-fox, as an Australian species (a much-debated matter, which will be enlarged upon later in this book) and places it in the *P. hypomelanus* group.

At first glance, the Torresian flying-fox looks very much like a small *Pteropus alecto*, the black flying-fox, also found on the island. However, after close examination and measurement of a number of specimens, consistent differences between the species emerge; for a start, the feet are longer and some of the teeth relatively larger in the new bat.

After the first submission of the description, including an examination of the animals' DNA, at least one scientist refereeing the paper was reluctant to accept that there was sufficient evidence presented to justify its separation as a full species from *Pteropus alecto*. However, Hall and Richards remain confident that the presentation of further material will establish the validity of the Torresian flying-fox as a new species.

Disagreements about the validity of a species can sometimes be based on the sample of specimens examined by the taxonomist. There can be considerable variation in form, colour or size between the sexes of a single species, amongst other things. Apart from this sexual dimorphism, basing a diagnosis on what are thought to be immature specimens can also lead to questions about the validity of a species. For example, Robert F. Tomes writes in the *Proceedings of the Zoological Society of London,* 1858, 'All the examples of *P. funereus* I have examined have had the unworn teeth of young individuals, and moreover exhibited further indications of immaturity, in the broad and flattened longitudinal crest of the cranium: in older examples this becomes prominent and acute. I regard the *P. funereus* as the young of *P. edulis*'. The name *Pteropus funereus* was eventually accepted as being synonymous with *P. edulis* by Peters in 1867 and again by Dobson in 1878. However, by 1912, *P. edulis* was regarded as a subspecies of *P. vampyrus,* a large and common Asian flying-fox. (Andersen, 1912.) *P. funereus* is now known as *P. alecto.*

Dr F. A. Jentinck, in 1883, provides us with another example in *Notes from the Leyden Museum,* vol. 5 . . . '*Pteropus wallacei* Gray. Gray's type specimen of this species is an immature individual and Prof. Peters thought it to be a young of *Pteropus personatus*. Dobson, however, in his *Catalogue of Chiroptera in the Collection of the British Museum* previously considered it a distinct species, the peculiar marking of the face being very different from those of *Pteropus personatus,* but he was unable to decide the question. Till now the type was the only known specimen. Therefore the specimen before me is of peculiar interest. It is a full-grown individual which exactly presents the same curious markings of the fur of the face as described by Gray and Dobson.' (See also Gray, 1866.)

In 1899 Matschie did some rearranging on the basis of *P. wallacei*'s dental equipment and put it into a genus of its own, *Styloctenium,* where it has remained. (Andersen, 1912; Honacki et al.) For a photograph and account of the extremely attractive *P. personatus* in the wild, I would refer readers to an article by Dr Tim Flannery of the Australian Museum, in *Geo* magazine (vol. 14, no. 1).

Before we diverge from the subject of describing species, description of colour for comparative purposes can be a problem when accuracy is important. In late 19th-century descriptions of animals one sees references to colours like 'Prout's brown'. This comes from Ridgway's book of standard colour reference, of which Oldfield Thomas wrote when describing *Pteropus admiralitatum* as a new species, in 1894: 'Nomenclature of Colours, 1886. The extreme difficulty of matching the uniform colours of a colour-plate and the grizzled and broken colours of an animal are so great that these determinations must be looked upon as merely approximate; but it would nevertheless be of great help to other workers if all describers would use some such stand of colours as is provided by Ridgway's valuable work'.

Just how frustrating the business of describing the colours of a specimen can be was brought home to me recently. It must have been a touch of artistic arrogance that led me to assume that this would be the least of my worries when reporting on the skin of the dusky flying-fox in the Natural History Museum in London. Otherwise, having travelled so far to look at it, I might have gone equipped with some sort of colour chart for comparison. The descriptions published by other authors vary and mention the possibility of fading, however, I wonder how much is attributable to individual perceptions of colour.

I also wonder about the wisdom of referring to the animal as the 'dusky' flying-fox on the basis of one skin. Having seen enormous variation in the fur colour of individual grey-headed flying-foxes, it occurs to me that the lone specimen might have been the only dark one of its kind.

No discussion of bats seems to get far these days without the question of their relationship to the primates being raised. In fact, it is remarkable how widespread the awareness of the current debate over bat phylogeny (evolutionary history) is — it crops up over dinner tables where one least expects it. Although Professor Jack Pettigrew's work on the similarities of the neural pathways of megachiropterans and those of primates, as presented at the First National Flying-fox Symposium (University of Queensland, 1986), was the trigger for my interest in *Pteropus*, the 'primate question' is still a topic I address with the greatest trepidation when asked.

Before dealing with the current debate, let us look briefly at the history of bat classification. Confusion over the place of bats amongst their fellow creatures is nothing new — it crosses centuries and cultures (see chapter 12). Many early sources, such as the Bible, refer to bats as birds rather than mammals and the theme of, 'Is it a bird, is it a mouse?' echoes through legend and literature. In the 17th century, John Ray at last placed bats squarely amongst the mammals, but still failed to find an ideal niche for them in his scheme of things and disposed of them in a ragbag of edentates (placental mammals in which the teeth are absent or greatly reduced) and insectivores as anomalous. (Smith, J. D., 1980)

This is less remarkable in the light of its pre-Darwinian timing. At that stage the accepted view was that the species being classified had arrived ready-made, rather than evolving over millions of years from primitive common ancestors to their present forms. So until the mid-19th century, classifications had more to do with 'pigeon-holing', or organising the natural world as one would sort a pack of cards on the basis of fairly superficial features. Prevailing philosophical and religious opinion also played a role in some cases.

By the time Linnaeus produced his *Systema Naturae* in its tenth edition (1758), he had been able to examine a wider variety of bats, including a species of *Pteropus*. Interestingly, this time the bats were accorded the status of a genus, *Vespertilio*, within the order Primates, along with humans, monkeys and lemurs. James Dale Smith suggests that Linnaeus based the grouping on the shared characteristics of a 'single pair of pectoral mammae; presence of well-developed clavicles [collar bones]; arboreal, frugivorous [fruit-eating] habits; position of the head on the vertebral column; hand-like structure of the wing of bats; and lemur-like appearance of the head of *Pteropus*.' To these, Pettigrew (1986) adds a further characteristic noted by Linnaeus, namely that of possessing a pendulous penis.

Very soon after this (1762), a French naturalist by the name of Brisson produced a second edition of his system of animal classification. This time the bats were divided into *Vespertilio* and *Pteropus*, the former being lumped in with the order Prosimia (lemurs) and the latter with Simia (monkeys). It was not until Blumenbach produced his reclassification in 1779–1780, that bats were recognised as a completely separate order, Chiroptera. (Smith, J. D., 1980)

A number of systems of classification were subsequently erected by various naturalists, retaining bats as an order on their own. The order was placed variously in loose association with non-human primates, and under the umbrellas of larger divisions — the flying mammals (Lacepede, 1799) and Cuvier's 'Les Carnassiers', which grouped together carnivores, insectivores and, interestingly, carnivorous marsupials, in 1800. And there, the fever of organisational activity seems to have abated temporarily, as far as bats were concerned. (Smith, J. D., 1980)

It is worth stopping to consider at this point that the 19th century brought with it a great age of discovery, in terms of the introduction of new species to European science. The sailing ships ranged widely on the business of trade and empire, carrying with them naturalist/collectors, official and amateur. In colonial outposts, the 'sportsman naturalists' were a source of specimens and, in some cases, information on the field biology of the animals they hunted. Young hopefuls of the East India Company were encouraged to attend the natural history classes of Robert Jameson, of Edinburgh University, to learn how to keep proper records of the flora and fauna they might encounter in the colonies. (Desmond & Moore, 1991.)

Temminck's *Monographies de Mammalogie* (1827) includes a description of *Pteropus keraudrenius* from Guam, in the Marianas, which was discovered and named by two prominent naturalists of the day who were accompanying a voyage under the command of Captain Freycinet. Observations of the animals in the field are included, '. . . Quoy and Gaimard report that this species is eaten in spite of the strong and disagreeable odour which it gives off. The bats fly in broad daylight and at rest they hang in trees rather than hiding away in holes or among rocky crags. The litter is of one young, which clings to its mother, even in flight. It has been named by the above mentioned naturalists in honour of M. Keraudren, inspector general of the health service of the Royal French Navy.'

The English systematist John E. Gray revised the arrangement of the bats three times from 1821 onward. First he considered the relationships of bats within their order. He assigned them to two orders, Fructivorae and Insectivorae, in his third class of Vertebrosa. In 1838, Gray revised this organisation, placing the bats in a family, Vespertilionidae, within the order of Primates. He then divided them (following Spix, 1823) according to whether or not they were equipped with 'nose leaves'. By 1866, Gray had reconsidered. This time he arranged the bats into five families which, with some adjustments, are the basis for the present classification. At this stage Darwin's *Origin of Species* had been in print for several years, though by no means universally accepted. The times were turbulent for science in Britain. Huxley and his cohorts were in the process of wresting it from the hands of the clergy and amateur gentlemen to re-create science as a profession.

Gray's arrangement was subsequently tampered with by various systematists, like Gill, who, in 1872, split the bats into suborders based on dietary habits — essentially those that fed on some form of animal life and those that fed on fruit. When, three years later, Dobson, author of the monumental catalogue of the British Museum's collection of Chiroptera, divided the bats into the suborders Microchiroptera and Megachiroptera, it was on virtually the same basis. The familial arrangements within the suborders was, however, somewhat different. He also suggested that the megachiropterans had evolved from microchiropteran ancestors. This view was contradicted by Winge in 1892, who reorganised the bats yet again and claimed that the ancestral stock of all bats was megachiropteran.

The fiddling did not finish there, and perhaps the most significant fiddler was Miller, in 1907. He retained Dobson's divisions — Megachiroptera and Microchiroptera — and set up within them the classification much as we know it today. He, incidentally, also plumped for megas as the original bats — the primitive form. And so it continued, with opinion shifting back and forth as to which groups of mammals share evolutionary links, which is derived from which, and how they all relate to each other, based on which criteria. With the advent of more sophisticated techniques, the scope for comparison goes beyond the traditional examination of an animal's skeletal and other more obvious features into

The Torresian flying-fox, discovered on Moa Island.

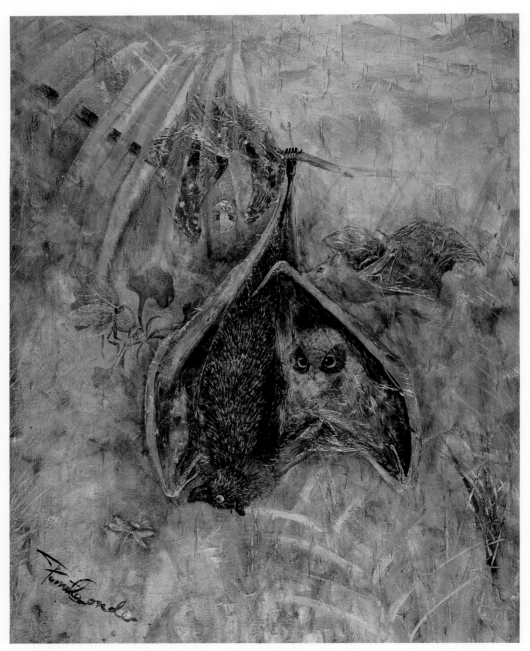

Nightlife on Moa Island: the black flying-fox (*Pteropus alecto*).

Colugo (*Cynocephalus*), the flying lemur.

the realm of DNA analysis. The results from the various methods of assessing relationships do not always tally.

An important issue related to the relationship between bats and primates is the question of where the dermopterans or colugos fit in. Miller (1907), without actually lumping it in with the Chiroptera, suggested that the colugo, the so-called flying lemur, which is not a true lemur and which glides rather than flies, could be viewed as an evolutionary stage of flight adaptation, already outstripped by the modern *Pteropus*. (Smith, J. D., 1980)

This brings us back to the work of Professor Jack Pettigrew. When examining some grey-headed flying-fox (*Pteropus poliocephalus*) brains, Pettigrew and his team discovered, to their surprise, that the visual pathways were typical of those of primates (see chapter 5). Further investigation showed that those of microchiropterans were more primitive and unlike the primate pathways. Further research showed that the motor (movement control) areas of the megachiropteran brain are primate-like, there being three of them rather than the two common amongst other mammals.

In their paper delivered at the First National Flying-fox Symposium in 1986, Pettigrew and Jamieson made the comment, 'Under the microscope, the affinities between a megachiropteran brain and a lemur brain are so striking that it is quite difficult to tell them apart! In other words, so far as one can tell from intricate details of the wiring of thousands of nerve cells, primates and megachiropterans shared a common ancestor not shared by any other group of mammals'. The important point to note is the 'common ancestor' – there is no suggestion here of a tribe of 'flying monkeys' such as those native to the fictional kingdom of Oz!

Are bats monophyletic? In other words, can we lump megachiropterans and microchiropterans together in one evolutionary bundle, confident that they are more closely related to one another than to any other group of mammals? Or are they diphyletic, with the megachiropterans more closely related to (sharing ancestry with) the primates? The accepted view is that chiropterans are the only mammals to have evolved truly mobile wings and 'powered' flight as opposed to gliding. This seems sufficient to unite them in the scheme of things. However, Pettigrew, amongst others, suggests that flight could have evolved twice, quite independently – a case of convergent evolution in animals not closely related but adapted to a common factor in lifestyle. The modification of the 'hand' is the most efficient origin of a mammalian wing. After all, other forms of locomotion have evolved in a wide range of animals. The macropods (kangaroos and wallabies), could be compared to the lagomorphs (rabbits and hares) or jerboas and the various species of hopping mice.

Pettigrew also cites the consistent basic differences between megachiropteran and microchiropteran wings. In microbats the metacarpals (equivalent to the bones of our hand) of the third and fourth digits are long in relation to the proximal phalanges (finger bones nearest the hand bones), whereas in megabats the bones in question are more similar in length. Pettigrew et al. (1987) suggest that this indicates evolutionary convergence from separate antecedents differing markedly in size. He suggests that flight evolved twice among the mammals, possibly in the Cretaceous era, when small insectivores progressed from leaping to flying in pursuit of airborne prey, and again in the Tertiary era, when a primitive primate evolved the ability to glide, as the colugo does, increasing the efficiency of its leaping foraging habits, and further developing into powered flight. The first case would represent the microchiropterans and the second the dermopterans and megachiropterans.

On the other hand, Simmons et al., in 1991, refuting Pettigrew's ideas in *Systematic Zoology* (vol. 40, 1991), state that, 'Megachiropteran and microchiropteran wings exhibit many derived similarities (including relative proportions of most limb elements), but only a few differences' and, 'There is no reason to believe that any mammal evolving membranous wings must use four long digits to support a wing membrane (three might function equally well).'

Pettigrew's critics turn the convergence argument around. Novacek and Simmons, opponents of the primate linkage, counter with the hypothesis that primates and megabats share neural characteristics associated with an evolved system of mammalian vision. This, they suggest, was forfeited by the microbats as echolocation evolved. (Goodman.) Such evolutionary reversal has been postulated as an important factor in explaining differences in other groups and its genetic basis was demonstrated experimentally in *Cavia* (Wright, 1977) (quoted in Simmons et al., 1991).

It has been suggested that the neuro-anatomical similarities between megachiropterans and primates could also be ascribed to convergence and the evidence of recent DNA analyses have been cited, suggesting that the two groups within the Chiroptera are genetically closer to one another than to any other group. This would imply that, quite independently of the primates, the megachiropterans, '"discovered" the exact details of the wiring in the primates in each of five baroque sets of nerve tracts involving tens of thousands of nerve cells'. (Pettigrew and Jamieson, 1986.)

The bodies of evidence on either side of the argument are, of course, far more complex than this, and will undoubtedly become more so as further investigations are carried out at the molecular level, using increasingly sophisticated techniques. I would recommend that readers wishing to weigh up the argument in greater detail should turn to a series of papers published in *Systematic Zoology* (vol. 40, no. 2, June, 1991). The four articles, two by Pettigrew and two by Robert J. Baker, Michael J. Novacek and Nancy B. Simmons, present critical analyses of the question from opposing points of view.

What we see in this very brief overview of mammalian systematics is ongoing change in the way humans make sense of the world. At times, conclusions have been drawn from insufficient evidence. In some cases science has been coloured by philosophy – the placing of man amongst the non-human primates was for some a stumbling block. It is not so very long since the followers of Darwin were pilloried from lectern and pulpit and lampooned in the popular press.

To return briefly to Pettigrew et al., I have not yet mentioned an important area of Pettigrew's evidence supporting the megachiropteran/primate link. Pettigrew and Jamieson refer to the work of two outstanding primatologists, Alison

Jolly (1985) and Le Gros Clark (1959) in defining what actually qualifies an animal for 'primateship'. The requirements can be divided into morphological (that is, relating to physical form) and behavioural traits, the combination of which distinguish the so-called conventional primates from other groups of mammals. These criteria are satisfied by megachiropterans, but not by microchiropterans. Another primatologist, Martin (1986), has put forward a set of 30 or so features that define a modern primate, more than 20 of which are evident in flying-foxes (some others need clarification and a few are absent). This is without taking the brain features into account. (Pettigrew and Jamieson, 1986.)

It was the mention of behavioural traits common to megachiropterans and primates which aroused my interest and set me looking for a group of flying-foxes at which to take a closer look.

The Birth of Roger

O
n 23 October, 1988, I decided that it was time to grasp the nettle and
begin what I envisaged as a one-year familiarisation study of a group of
grey-headed flying-foxes at the Healesville Sanctuary in Victoria. In
1993 I am still at it and, as often happens, finding two questions for every answer
about the bats' behaviour and biology.

For a time I had considered studying a free-living group of the same species in
the Royal Melbourne Botanic Gardens. However, as I was particularly interested in
how individuals associate within a group and whether factors such as mating
seasons, rearing of young and so forth affect this, I took the easier option. At the
sanctuary I could learn to recognise individuals without resorting to banding or
marking the animals, I could put together some sort of life history for each bat and,
confined as they are in a spacious walk-through aviary, visibility is less
problematical. All this was very fine in theory — in practice it proved less
straightforward.

The study began on a still, clear, Sunday morning. The Healesville Sanctuary is a bush park-style zoo, nestling at the foot of the mountains about 60 kilometres northeast of Melbourne. The plangent chiming of bellbirds seemed to bounce through the gently warmed air and rebound from the wattles and native mint bushes lining the pathways. I passed the dingoes, flashes of russet-tinged ochre fur contrasting sharply with the emerald green of still-wet grass, as they chased each other, cavorting in their enclosure. A moment later the unmistakable short, staccato 'quacking' call of a flying-fox drew me to the aviary next door.

The moment I entered, my eye was caught by one of the 12 bundles of fur and leather sunning themselves suspended from the wire mesh roof at the far end of the exhibit. Eleven small dark bodies were twirling gently in the sun, allowing it to warm the taut skin of their tightly wrapped wings and enliven the rich, burnt sienna mantle of fur surrounding their necks and shoulders. To the left, and slightly apart from the others, one bat hung with its wings stiffly fanned across its front, assiduously grooming behind this shield of dark, almost glossy membrane.

My mind snapped back to the previous year, and the huge mixed camp of grey-headed and black flying-foxes I had been watching on the bank of the Brisbane River at Indooroopilly. It was, as one would expect at that time of year, seething with females at variously advanced stages of pregnancy, or carrying young. There it became clear to me that, although flying-foxes are nocturnal feeders, there was much to be gained by studying their social activity within the camp by day.

The fruit bat aviary, which is also occupied by a pair of squalling green catbirds and elegant little black-faced wood swallows, is one of the most attractive in Healesville Sanctuary. A path winds past a central pond with its miniature gravelly beach and plantings of tall grasses and ferns. Suspended over this area, beneath a covered section of roof, is the four-sided food and water hopper, which is raised and lowered by a pulley system from the side of the cage. Lining the path are shrubby trees, the odd tree fern and two palms with fans reaching to the wire mesh of the roof. Outside, a huge gum towers skyward, providing a perch for a pair of wild wedge-tailed eagles when they tire of soaring above their territory. Strangely enough, although they are one of the natural predators of flying-foxes, the bats never seemed concerned, while I sat watching through the roof mesh, as the eagles wheeled overhead.

A log lying beside the path towards the middle of the cage offered a convenient, if ergonomically unsound, perch from which to observe the bats without upsetting them. From there I soon began catching glimpses of the chest of the wing-shielding bat. Through the binoculars it was just possible to make out the damp, dark form of an infant, its head buried in the mother's axilla as it clung to

Grey-headed flying-fox (*Pteropus poliocephalus*) with young.

her nipple, inordinately large feet with scimitar claws groping for a hold in her belly fur as she groomed vigorously. From her vulva hung what appeared to be the severed umbilicus, indicating that she had not yet expelled the placenta.

The claws and milk teeth of a young flying-fox (*Pteropus*). Pads under the claws prevent damage to the mother's skin as the infant clings to her. The recurved milk teeth also assist the infant in gripping its mother.

When flying-foxes give birth, the head is delivered first. The infant has its eyes open and is able to vocalise, which it indeed does in some cases, even before the delivery is completed. It seems that a pause of between ten minutes and one hour in the labour is not unusual once the head has emerged, and during this time mother and young may begin to communicate. As the birth is completed the female guides her offspring into a position where it can reach the nipple to suckle. She does this using her mouth and one foot.

The infant is dependent on its mother not only for sustenance, but also for the regulation of its body temperature during the first three or so weeks of its life. The young are born without fur on the belly, chest, and the area beneath the chin, and are only very sparsely haired around the muzzle. To help them cling to their mother until fully furred and thus able to deal with their own thermoregulation, the young have recurved milk teeth for grasping the nipple and additional hooks on the inner curve of their claws to allow them to hold securely to the mother's belly fur even when she is in flight. The hook-like protuberances are eventually shed.

Between glimpses of the infant at its mother's breast, I began trying to sort out the rest of the animals suspended above my head. The animals nearest to the mother were a large, dark male with a band on his right thumb and a female with a pea-sized hole in one wing. The mother herself was lighter in colour than the others and had short, clipped-looking ears. This was the beginning of a long process of familiarisation. I watched as the others rotated and swayed gently, as clouds passed between the sun and their bodies, briefly allowing the breeze to chill them. With a vague idea of how to recognise three animals, I still needed to find sufficient easily spotted peculiarities amongst the other ten in order to record who was doing what, and to whom.

The most obvious difficulty was that when at rest, flying-foxes hang with their wings wrapped around their bodies, thumbs on the inside, and chins tucked up against their chests. When active, they are anything but easy to follow quickly enough with binoculars to note things like metal thumb bands, missing thumb tips, and the various facial and ear characteristics. Ears eventually became quite useful points of recognition, but their shapes needed careful monitoring to note changes due to scarring. It would be many weeks before I could readily identify all the members of the group no matter what the pace of their activities.

Part of the process of fixing individual identities firmly enough in memory to record their interactions is naming the individuals. Some people prefer to stay with number or letter codes, to avoid any possible compromise to the objectivity of their observations by subjective personal associations with 'word' names. This was my attitude to begin with. The mother became 010, referring to the standard three-digit system of recording groups and sexes of zoo animals. The number of males is in first position, females in second and unsexed young in third. Hence, one female: 0.1.0; one young: 0.0.1, and so on. At that stage the group of flying-foxes was 7.5.1. The female with the holed wing became HW and the male with the thumb band, I listed as BRW1 (Band Right Wing 1). By the time I had added 010B and her offspring 001B, BRW2, BRWF (F for female) and LBW (Left Banded Wing) the system was becoming unwieldy and I decided to use an obvious physical characteristic, like Split for a male with one ear split from tip to base and Spot for a female whose aluminium fingerling tag in her ear showed through her fur as a whitish spot. Scruff was fairly self-explanatory.

The point is that such names are far easier to associate automatically with individuals when you are trying to observe them and quickly note down what is going on. There is, of course, no opportunity to go back over an interaction to check on which animals are involved unless one is working with a video camera.

Over the next few days the female with the hole in her wing, HW, continued to show a degree of interest in the mother and infant, and was tolerated up to a point. However, moving into the zone less than 20 centimetres or so around the mother evoked a swift vocal rebuff, sometimes combined with a hooking blow from the wrist and thumb and even brief pursuit. Once the critical distance had been restored, the nursing female would quickly settle to rest with wings folded, or attend to her offspring. Whatever her purpose in approaching the mother and young, I never saw HW stand her ground or persist when rebuffed by 010.

Males were similarly dealt with and likewise retreated from the sharp vocalisations and hooking blows. On the third day three males began to pester 010, also bickering amongst themselves. Two approached her with penises erect, however, if attempted mating was the intention, they were easily discouraged.

Male grey-headed flying-foxes do in fact carry viable sperm in the epidydimus throughout the year, however, most females do not seem to ovulate and conceive before April in the course of a limited though intensive mating season between March and May. There are exceptions, as is shown by out of season births in captivity. In the Healesville group there are records of three February births. The gestation period of six months indicates that successful matings took place in September or thereabouts.

By the fourth day more individuals were becoming familiar to me in terms of what I would later recognise as significant relationships within the group. As HW moved away from the others after ten minutes of intermittent sexual overtures from one of the males, she passed the area directly above my head and met a previously unobserved fourteenth bat. It was a young male, hanging outside the normal roosting area of the colony. The two met without the vocalisation or rebuff I had expected, then HW continued on her way. This particular male was to prove extremely interesting.

Although the walk-through bat aviary is spacious enough to house a much larger colony, it was soon apparent that the flying-foxes preferred to use only a relatively small area at one end as a roost and loosely grouped themselves on either side of the central ridge and towards the apex of the sloping triangles beyond it (see diagram on p. 159). It was unusual for an animal to leave the security of the group and move further from the others than the first roof section, even when harassed. (Of course this changed at feeding time, when all moved to the central covered area to the food hoppers.) It was interesting, in view of the space available, that 'walking' — using the feet, or feet and thumbs — was the preferred option to flying, unless the pressure was extreme. Flying is, of course, an expensive form of locomotion in terms of energy consumption.

On the same day that I was introduced to SM (Small Male), the outsider, by HW, I also noticed a pair of light-coloured females in the central area. At first I assumed that one was a male, as it was assiduously grooming the genital area of the other with its tongue, which is typical of flying-fox foreplay. I was more than a little surprised to find, during a pause in the proceedings, that both animals were of the same sex. The recipient of these unusual attentions was Spot, the female sporting a fingerling tag in her left ear and a distinctly shortened right ear. Her partner, who bore a distinct resemblance to her in colouring and head shape, was duly christened Fang, in deference to her protruding left canine tooth. This was the first instance I saw of adult animals in close and apparently amicable contact with each other.

Within a couple of days another relationship between apparently adult animals became obvious. After sitting on my pathside log for 20 minutes or so, watching the last of some out-of-season sexual activity, my attention was drawn to what I at first took to be two females, sparring with their thumbs. Gradually they moved across the roof, from the first quadrant to the second, still hooking intermittently at one another. Two minutes from the beginning of the encounter, they stopped and settled to quiet mutual grooming. I wondered whether their pattern would follow that of Spot and Fang. To my astonishment, the larger animal, definitely a female, began assuming the wing-shielding posture I had observed in 010 shortly after giving birth to her infant. The wing-shielding continued as the larger bat groomed the smaller, the latter being encompassed in her wings and apparently nuzzling in search of a nipple. Six minutes later they were at rest, the smaller one enfolded completely by the large female.

Thus they remained for a short period, until the large female, distinguished by a metal band on her left thumb and a missing tip to her left ear, opened both her eyes and her wings. The other bat was revealed, with its head buried in her armpit, presumably attached to the nipple and making no attempt to move. After five minutes hanging quietly like this, the large female, duly dubbed 010B, broke away, swinging herself by thumbs and feet across the quadrants of the roof. She was followed by her erstwhile partner and stopped to spar briefly, finally deterring the persistent bat and moving alone to rest, wing-wrapped in Triangle 1. All the while I sat 6 metres below, vainly trying to confirm the sex of the smaller animal. It is no simple task, trying to follow a moving bat whilst endeavouring to focus binoculars on its genitalia.

It was another two weeks before the matter became clear — the over-aged suckler was a male and, I eventually worked out, must be SM, the outsider from the group encountered by HW on the same day that Spot and Fang had been identified. On the day I finally established his identity, I had returned to the enclosure briefly after an hour's break from observations to find 010B quietly nursing him at her breast. My notes also remark on 010B's rotundity at the time. This may have had some bearing on the situation, as we shall see.

The activity between 010B and SM led me to suspect that he might be her previous season's offspring, which close examination of the sanctuary's records and a certain amount of deduction subsequently confirmed. It appeared that he had been born in February 1988 and was therefore eight months old. 010B's acceptance of his return to maternal comforts seemed less surprising in the light of this (I later found that she was a 'late weaner', allowing her offspring to stay on board for up to six months) and lasted until 10 November. On the following day she gave birth to an infant, provisionally christened 001B until its sex could be determined.

The situation between SM and his mother was not unique. In discussing it with Helen Luckhoff, who has spent many years working with this species in

Brisbane, I learned that the adult daughter of one of her captive animals returned regularly to suckle her mother, or attempt to do so, in the days preceding the birth of subsequent young.

In the meantime, the infant 001 had been developing apace. He could be seen shuffling around on his mother's chest, changing from one nipple to the other as she hung with wings open to the sun. She seemed aware of being observed and would frequently turn away or enfold the youngster in her wings if I pointed a camera at them. This did not help my attempts to keep a record of 001's development. Her mothering style subsequently proved rather more protective and less relaxed than that of 010B.

From time to time 001's tiny, almost transparent wing would droop beneath or between his mother's wings. To begin with, there was little evidence of control or coordination. However, by his sixth day 001 was able to flap one wing as it escaped the maternal embrace. By his fourteenth day he was first seen holding the roof wire with one foot, then hanging by both feet for short periods. By this time 001's front was becoming furred and he was about halfway to the stage where, in the wild, he could be 'parked' in a nursery tree rather than carried around all night on foraging flights.

In spite of this, it would still be some months before the youngster would be weaned, and for the next few weeks most of his time was spent firmly attached to his mother's nipple, even when hanging by his own feet. It is common in breeding colonies to see what look like three-legged flying-foxes, as the foot of a completely enfolded but sizeable youngster protrudes beside those of its mother to grasp the branch.

On 20 November I left the Healesville flying-foxes to their own devices for a month, to go on the field trip described in chapter 1. I also wanted to look at some wild flying-fox camps in Queensland and on the New South Wales coast, where I was also interested in the problems and attitudes of fruit farmers. Somehow my orchardist friends in Nambucca Heads were less than delighted with the 'Bats are Beautiful' t-shirts I brought as gifts, and threatened to disown me.

The 'Batty Boat'

The *Mirimar* left Hayle's Wharf to cruise up the Brisbane River via Davies Park to Indooroopilly at four-thirty in the afternoon. The 150 passengers included ten members of the Queensland Wildlife Preservation Society's Western Branch, a large and lively group of teenage girl guides, and me. This was my second visit to Brisbane on flying-fox business and I had been invited to see some pteropid public relations in action.

At one end of the elegantly appointed pink and white lower-deck lounge a demountable walk-in cage had been set up and furnished with six flying-foxes — blacks and grey-headeds — from the University of Queensland's colony. The university's captive breeding colony is the largest of its kind in the world, comprising around 225 individuals: 50 *Pteropus alecto*, 65 *P. scapulatus*, and the rest *P. poliocephalus*.

As well as flying-foxes, the passengers were introduced to Puggles the three-footed echidna reared by Helen Luckhoff, a woman well known in Brisbane for her rehabilitation of orphaned wildlife. He had been found in a ploughed field, with one hind foot so badly damaged that amputation was necessary. The operation was performed with great success by wildlife veterinarian Rosemary Booth, who, having considerable experience as a fixer of flying-foxes, was also on board helping out. This was the first time I had met Rosie. As we discussed the Healesville flying-foxes, neither of us realised that a year or so later they would be reaping the benefit of her experience when she became the sanctuary's vet. In fact, without her skill, two of the present members of the group would very probably be defunct.

Four of the 'Batty Boat' flying-foxes were tame, hand-reared animals that provided an opportunity for direct contact with the public. This was achieved by people either entering the cage under supervision, or viewing the animals as they were taken out and handled by Dr Len Martin, and by Lorraine Little, who looked after the university's colony.

Len, a tall, thin, 'former' Englishman with the air of a hyperactive mantis and a wryly twisted sense of humour, is a reproductive physiologist and senior lecturer at the University of Queensland. He and his students have produced an impressive body of work on flying-fox reproduction, which will be discussed a little later. Len and his wife Kay are also energetic campaigners for the conservation of wildlife and work hard on these boat trips to improve the public's understanding of flying-foxes.

As the boat chugged quietly towards Indooroopilly, the afternoon light faded into dusk. We reached the mangroves lining the golf course where restless black silhouettes stirred amongst the bare tops of trees against a vivid sunset sky. I wondered why in this country, so eager to sell itself to the tourist, so little is made of spectacles like this. As the light gently expired, allowing a glowing, bruised darkness to flush the sky, the first lazily flapping shapes appeared overhead, disappearing in the direction of the bridge and the lights of Brisbane beyond. In summer, tens of thousands of these quiet, ancient spectres leisurely pass in their Gothic splendour over the fuming, flickering city as its scurrying inhabitants hustle to shut it down.

On the upper deck of the boat, passengers hurried from side to side, following the flight of the bats, as ever more emerged from the camp and headed towards their feeding grounds around Brisbane and the Brisbane Forest Park. Occasionally one of the huge bats would skim the surface of the river, drinking on the wing. In the background, Len Martin's voice could be heard on the public address system, delivering a running commentary on the spectacle, interspersed with an informal lecture on flying-fox biology and conservation.

Much of our knowledge of the general biology of Australian flying-foxes has its basis in the work of two men. Flying-foxes appear to be the first native Australian mammals to be made the subject of a major publicly funded study. Francis Ratcliffe was appointed by the state governments of New South Wales and Queensland in 1929 to investigate claims that flying-foxes represented a serious threat as orchard pests. After pursuing the matter for two years Ratcliffe published an 80-page report in which their reputation was vindicated. Much of this monumental scientific undertaking was carried out by travelling up and down the east coast of Australia on a motorbike. The results are still widely regarded as the definitive study of this subject. (Hall, 1986.) Ratcliffe later wrote a less formal account of his work in *Flying Fox and Drifting Sand* (Angus & Robertson, 1947), a book full of life and charm in its description of people and country encountered in his pursuit of the bats.

In the mid-1960s, John Nelson, this time travelling by car, also covered many miles studying flying-foxes for a PhD thesis. The scope of his work was extensive, covering behaviour, vocal communication, aspects of physiology and population movements. In fact, he invented the 'pink bat' long before the commercial variety began proliferating in the roofs of Australia as insulation. In order to identify his group of study animals and follow their movements, Nelson arranged an early morning 'air raid', spraying the flying-foxes with rhodamine red dye. The sight of his study animals probably did the local Temperance Movement a power of good. It certainly raised the flying-fox consciousness of the citizens of Brisbane for a time.

Many other researchers are now at work in the field, but there is much still to be discovered about *Pteropus* in Australia and the part flying-foxes are playing in the environment. As I listened to Len Martin summarising the state of our knowledge for the passengers, I reflected on the inherent difficulties of studying animals which are not only primarily nocturnal, but go about their business mostly high in the crowns of trees and, on top of that, enjoy a mobility extraordinary for mammals in their ability to fly. I wondered what had possessed me to become involved with such thoroughly inconvenient animals.

A few minutes later, back in the lounge of the *Mirimar*, such thoughts were dismissed. I stood watching the tame flying-foxes, alert but confident, apparently consumed with typical pteropid curiosity about the hair, clothes, jewellery and cameras of the humans surrounding them. It is not hard to believe that they are Australia's most intelligent native mammal and one of the most adaptable.

The sharp foxy muzzles and delicately probing tongues investigated every novelty. Thumbs shot out to pull closer items of interest spotted by the shining dark eyes, set like highly polished beads in their fur. A flying-fox can manipulate remarkably well with a combination of thumbs and mouth. I have often had earrings swiftly and gently removed by a flying-fox, or my hair delicately but persistently combed with a thumb claw.

The bats' interest in Len was of a somewhat different nature. For some reason the flying-foxes seemed compelled to urinate on him as frequently and copiously as possible. I watched in fascination as one male hauled himself across the inside of the wire cage to poke its penis through the mesh and administer another dousing to

Grey-headed flying-fox (*Pteropus poliocephalus*).

Len's already thoroughly damp clothes, while a female attended similarly to his arm as she crawled around on it. Perhaps Len looked in need of sprucing up. Flying-foxes of both sexes quite commonly groom their fur with urine. The purpose of this is not known, although it could have something to do with reinforcing identifying odours for social and sexual purposes. When this is done, the animal remains in the usual feet-up position. Ordinary voiding of urine or faeces is performed in a head-up, feet-down posture, while the bat hangs by its thumbs. This is a handy piece of information if one intends to spend time under trees full of flying-foxes; at least there is time to get out of the way.

My first sight of a major *Pteropus* summer camp was from the other side of the Indooroopilly mangroves. It was early November in 1987. The sun was already biting the clear, quiet morning as I crossed the smooth lawns of the golf links. It occurred to me for the first time that field work could be dangerous. Snakes and sundry biters in the bush had never seemed much of a bother compared to the prospect of being felled by a stray golf ball in suburban Brisbane.

Having negotiated what had become in my mind the missile range, the smell of cut grass was overpowered by a wave of richly flying-fox-scented air rising from the edge of the overgrown valley. As I stepped through the dense green tangle at its margin, it was as though the curtain had lifted on an opera. Thousands of flying-foxes hung and clambered about in the bare tree tops, fur glistening and dark wings gleaming dully in the sun. More wheeled overhead and down in the valley, landing heavily amongst the branches to a chorus of reproof from the incumbents.

This was a mixed camp of black and grey-headed flying-foxes, species commonly found sharing summer camps with each other, or with little reds, where

The powerful owl (*Ninox strenua*) preys on flying-foxes.

Ring-tailed lemurs (*Lemur catta*); their brains share characteristics with those of flying-foxes.

their ranges overlap. Spectacled flying-foxes are sometimes found in the same roosts as blacks, however, according to Greg Richards' observations, they do not associate with little reds, even though their ranges overlap.

My guide on this first visit to Indooroopilly was Les Hall, who began by pointing out the roosting patterns within the camp. It was not simply a seething mass of fur and leather, it was a society. Some areas were occupied predominantly by males. This was not difficult to discern. 'They like to keep the brassware out and polished', as Les obligingly pointed out. As mentioned earlier, male flying-foxes are opportunistic copulators, but it was too early in the season for them to be establishing individual territories for serious procreational activity. Nevertheless, their sunbathing was punctuated by scuffles and bickering over positions.

Branches were marked by rubbing on scent from the shoulder or scapular glands. These are actually modifications of sebaceous glands, opening into hair follicles and secreting a fatty substance called sebum. This is also the origin of the characteristic musky odour. Both sexes have these glands, but they are larger in the males. Nelson found that the size of the glands in males and females varies, the peak size coinciding with the months when mating territories are being established and defended.

In other areas females had congregated, many of the blacks already carrying large youngsters and most of the grey-headeds heavily pregnant (although the breeding seasons of these species more or less coincide). John Nelson found in Queensland that the females are usually the first to return to the traditional camps in September, to give birth and begin rearing their young. This is not always the case according to the work done on colonies in New South Wales by Kerryn Parry-Jones and Michael Augee. In at least one study area, the young are generally born in small 'birthing' colonies located near food sources, before the large mating camp is formed.

S.H. Prater comments in his *Book of Indian Animals* on the preponderance of flying-fox births occurring immediately prior to the main season of flower and fruit production. The mating season for flying-foxes on India's west coast in the vicinity of Bombay falls between October and December, with births peaking between March and April. A similar situation exists amongst the black, grey-headed and spectacled flying-foxes of Australia, which mate in autumn (see chapter 9) and give birth in spring. By contrast, the more nomadic little reds generally give birth around April or early May, in a cycle six months out of phase with the others. (Hall and Richards, 1979.)

The Indooroopilly camp is one of the most exciting 'wildlife spectacles' I have seen anywhere in the world. The flying-foxes hang out in the full sun, alternately grooming their infants and enfolding them, basking with wings tucked back 'under their arms' as it were, or stretched to their full span of a metre or so. Sometimes one wing would be extended and dropped to fan gently like an oddly shaped punkah. The wings are important in temperature regulation, being well supplied with blood vessels separated from the air only by the thin membrane. They act similarly to a car's radiator; the blood is cooled and passes back into the body, lowering its temperature.

Australian flying-fox colonies vary enormously in size, in the case of some summer camps, more than a million animals may occupy an area. These are probably the largest gatherings of land mammals seen in this country. The largest colonies are those of the little reds, which may number in the millions. Les Hall and Greg Richards wrote of a camp in the Queensland Gulf country that was 5 kilometres long and 50 metres wide. The little reds' habit of roosting clustered tightly together gives some idea of the vast number of individuals likely to be present in such a large area.

Getting reasonably accurate counts of flying-foxes in a colony is problematical. Researchers differ in their methods, which range from counting streams of bats during the evening flyout to making audio-tape recordings of the vocalisations in the camp during the day. (Parry-Jones and Augee, 1992.) In smaller colonies it is possible to count animals in the roost trees, although experience has shown that this method frequently leads to appreciable underestimates. More often than I care to admit, I have marched up and down the paths of the Royal Melbourne Botanic Gardens, one hand holding the binoculars steady, the other cradling the back of my skull (try it and you will know why) counting aloud as I spotted bats in the tree tops. Visitors probably think it is some fringe form of street theatre, but I do not find it entertaining when I come up with a different total on each circuit.

The usual location of camps near water — sometimes on river banks, sometimes on islands or amongst mangroves — may be a matter of navigation. For an animal travelling by air, landmarks are important; finding a camp located in a sea of green forest would be far more difficult. From the air, much of Australia's northern tip resembles a giant box of tightly packed broccoli. Spectacled flying-foxes moving in the area between Innisfail and the Atherton Tablelands seem to use the Palmerston Valley as a visual navigation aid and use a stopping off point on the Beatrice River. (Hall and Richards, 1991.)

Spectacled flying-foxes are more restricted than the other species in their distribution, less inclined to mix with other species in camps and in some cases colonies remain at traditional roost sites year round. There is an inconsistency in movement patterns in that some sites are used seasonally, for example, in the vicinity of Atherton as summer camps, where, as in *P. poliocephalus* and *P. alecto*, young are born and raised to independence. However, some colonies remain in a

Little red flying-fox (*Pteropus scapulatus*).

year-round camp even for breeding, which could be influenced by seasonality of food sources. *P. conspicillatus* favours dense vegetation for roosting, in rainforest, riverine rainforest, paperbark swamp or mangroves. Although *P. alecto* in the same range chooses physically similar sites, they are less restricted in their choice of locality. *P. conspicillatus* sites were never more than 6.5 kilometres from rainforest whereas *P. alecto* colonies were found up to 155 kilometres from rainforest tracts. McNab (1982) found that the metabolic rates of the large megachiropterans are high, thus for those obliged to comb rainforest tracts in search of fruit as the main component of their diet, it is energetically economical to reduce the commuting distance between camp and foraging areas. (Richards, 1990.)

Flying-foxes are also more urbanised mammals than is generally realised. There is a colony in the Royal Melbourne Botanic Gardens and a sizeable camp is located in a pocket of bushland nestling discreetly in a small valley in Sydney's northern suburbs. Many dwellers of these cities are well-acquainted with the large dark shapes of flying-foxes sailing with silent, leisurely wingbeats through the skyscape of the city night. M. Brock Fenton comments in his book *Just Bats* on the presence of flying-fox camps amidst the cacophony of traffic noise and human activity in the centres of some Indian cities, where to some extent the bats enjoy a measure of protection by religious customs. My first sighting of bats in India was indeed in a busy and popular centre — a wild colony of flying-foxes festooned the branches of a huge tree just inside the front entrance of Bombay Zoo.

When large groups of animals get together, it is not generally just to have a party — there is some sort of biological advantage involved. Not that I am suggesting that, with the arrival of spring, a young flying-fox's fancy consciously turns to being generous with its genes — with as many of its fellows as possible. There is, however, a genetic advantage for the species in keeping the gene pool as large as possible. One of the great problems with species whose numbers have dwindled is that inbreeding is likely to occur and the proportion of congenital defects within the population increases.

Another potential advantage of congregating over a fairly protracted period is the sharing of knowledge. Bees, also colonial animals with a structured society, communicate information about the location of food sources amongst their members. Some primates pass on experience-based information to other group members. Fletemeyer's work published in 1978 describes how a male baboon (*Papio ursinus*), highly ranked with its social unit, experienced a certain fruit as being poisonous. He later made aggressive threats to juveniles and sub-adults who approached similar experimentally presented fruit. Thus group members learned to avoid it.

Flying-foxes are highly communicative animals, both visually and vocally. Nelson was able to identify a repertoire of at least 20 different vocalisations. It is not difficult to see how young flying-foxes would learn things like basic social rituals by experience within the colony. However, it is probable that they also acquire knowledge of feeding areas and routes for migration from mature animals. Hall and Richards cite evidence for this and offer some clue as to the transmission of such information in observations of spectacled flying-foxes. At times, through the summer months, groups have been seen flying out of the camp, with a large animal in the lead. These small groups stay together, emitting high-pitched contact calls as they fly. It is thought that it could be a case of older experienced individuals guiding youngsters to foraging areas.

Animals living in large groups enjoy certain advantages as far as the likelihood of being picked off by predators goes. In grey-headed flying-fox summer camps the peripheral areas are usually occupied by 'guard groups'. These are unmated animals, not preoccupied with rearing young, maintaining territories, or copulating. The central area of the camp, where the greatest concentrations of bats roost, is typically open to the sky, with most of the vegetation being stripped of foliage. This clearing is not necessarily intentional; flying-foxes are not the most graceful creatures when it comes to landing — they tend to crash into the vegetation, doing a certain amount of incidental leaf stripping in the process. In some cases, however, leaves are chewed. John Nelson saw grey-headed flying-foxes in camp, biting the leaves of roost trees without actually breaking them off. Some of the trees, when examined, had toothmarks in all their leaves. Sometimes the leaves are eaten, even the tough leaves of mangroves. (Hall and Richards, 1991.)

Clearing is not only of advantage to the flying-foxes — sometimes the vegetation benefits in the longer term. Mangrove seedlings, for instance, gain access to sunlight and the new growth is fertilised by the animals' droppings.

Intruders into the camp area are usually located by sound first. You will often see the ears of an apparently sleeping flying-fox rotating independently of each other, alert to unfamiliar noises. The simple 'horn' shape of the outer ear, or pinna, helps to amplify sound (see chapter 5). Once the animal has been alerted, the source of the disturbance is located visually. Warnings can be conveyed by both visual and vocal signals.

Of course not all potential predators are particularly noisy. The major consumers of flying-foxes are pythons, goannas, wedge-tailed and sea eagles, powerful owls and crocodiles, the latter occasionally snatching bats as they skim the water to drink. Power lines also prove detrimental to the wellbeing of flying-foxes from time to time. However, the most significant killer of flying-foxes, both directly and through destruction of habitat, is humans.

Alfred Searcy gives an interesting account of predation by an eagle in his book *In Australian Tropics*, published in 1907. He writes in the chapter 'At Timber Creek': 'When passing through a belt of mangroves further down the river, we started thousands and thousands of flying-foxes. Soon a great eagle appeared on the scene, and having spotted a fine plump fox, started to cut it out. Away the victim went, dodging among its fellows. Every now and then we could hear a plaintive cry, as the eagle followed it up. The others did not seem to take the least notice. When the creature was fairly out of the crowd the eagle pounced on it and sailed away.'

Chris Pavey of the University of Queensland found that black and grey-headed flying-foxes were the most significant prey species in the diet of a pair of powerful owls (*Ninox strenua*) near Brisbane during his 1989–90 study. Although this was the first time that flying-foxes had been identified as a major item in the diet of this species, there have been many reports of powerful owls preying on them. A powerful owl has become resident in the Melbourne Botanic Gardens, perhaps coincidentally, but perhaps it has something to do with the presence of grey-headed flying-foxes. In 1896, Lucas made mention of the 'Great Winking Owl' preying upon flying-foxes, but regrettably gives no scientific name for the owl.

Popular opinion has it that flying-foxes in Australia have it made — huge colonies with relatively few predator problems and not only the nation's forests, but also the fruit growers' crops to feed on. Do not be too sure. The evidence suggests that, at least in the southeastern coastal region, flying-fox populations have declined dramatically since European settlement. Food becomes more scarce as habitat is progressively lost and, as forests are fragmented, the seasonal patterns of flying-fox movements are interrupted.

In some cases the distances that must be covered in moving from one feeding ground to another simply become too great, so bats become 'trapped' in regional pockets. (Hall and Richards, 1991.) This was seen in the Brisbane area in the winter of 1990, when the eucalyptus blossoming failed. More than 1000 flying-foxes were found dead. Starving animals were seen feeding in daylight, many on unripe fruit, the toxins in which may have been the cause of some of the deaths. There were also instances of blindness, abortions and hydrocephaly (in infants) observed that season. One desperate animal was seen trying to feed on peaches not much bigger than peas. (Martin, L., Hall, L., Luckoff, H., Kelly, R. and O'Brien, G., unpublished.) The conflict of fruit growers' interests with those of the flying-foxes will be dealt with in chapter 11.

I left Queensland, filled with naive enthusiasm for my project. There were seasoned bat men to turn to for guidance — the bat fraternity is generous with moral support for the novice. Les Hall suggested that if I intended to fool around with flying-foxes anyway, I could make myself useful by writing a book — a popular account of *Pteropus*.

Having experienced the complexity of a wild colony 500 000 to 600 000 strong amongst the mangroves and mud, studying a group of 13 flying-foxes a mere 6 metres over my head seemed a doddle. How easily an optimist can be deceived!

CHAPTER 5

Bat Senses

When I returned to Healesville after four weeks away in the field, I found that not only had 001 grown considerably, but another infant had arrived. The large female, 010B, previously seen allowing the young male SM to suckle, had given birth. I later learned from the keeping staff that this had taken place on 2 December, so the infant was now two-and-a-half weeks old. I was immediately curious to see how 010B's mothering style would differ from that of 010 and whether there would be much variation in the development of the infants.

It was immediately apparent that 010B was a more relaxed mother than the older female 010. There could be a number of factors at play in this, quite apart from so-called 'personality' differences. For a start, confidence could relate to the animal's social status and that of her associate(s). I had already gained a distinct impression that the group was roughly divided into 'left-siders' and 'right-siders' (relative to the centre ridge of the cage roof). Although I was mapping the roosting positions and areas used by the bats each day, it was not until I could positively identify each individual that I was able to confirm my impression. The matter was further complicated when, on particularly hot afternoons, the usual arrangements were abandoned by most individuals, as they sought shade in a small triangular area of roof not usually used by any of them, except LBW, a mature male (see map on page 159).

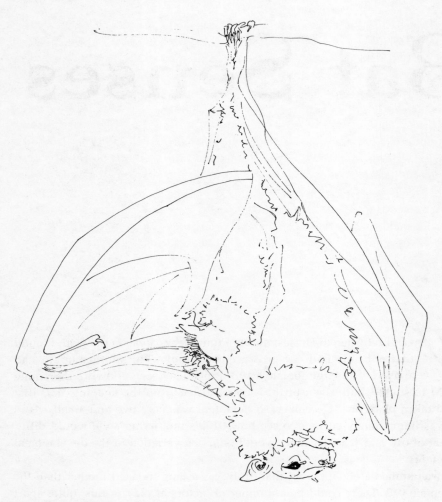

Grey-headed flying-fox (*Pteropus poliocephalus*) with young.

010B was (and is) one of the right-siders, frequently taking up a position in the centre ridge, or near to it in Far Quadrant 1. My first sight of her baby was quite different to the awkward dodging and darting to catch glimpses of 010's infant. 010B dangled casually by her toes, with one thumb hooked through the roof mesh. The other wing was pulled back, exposing her chest and the little one clinging tightly to her fur. This 'If you've got it, flaunt it' attitude seemed characteristic of 010B, as I watched her over the years. It certainly made observation of her offspring much easier.

The other right-siders included BRW2, a large and apparently dominant male. With some difficulty and much patience I had managed to sort out the fact that there were two males wearing bands on their right thumbs and looking very similar. They were much of a size and both dark-coloured with heavy, slightly blunt muzzles. They caused me considerable confusion until I discovered that BRW2 had a shortened left ear. BRW1 was the male I had seen hanging around 010 in the period following the birth of her baby — he was a left-sider. As I became more familiar with the animals as individuals, I realised that BRW1 also had a slightly lighter face than BRW2. With time and nearer acquaintance, I was often surprised to think that members of the group had once looked much like one another to me.

The basic idea with banding was that females should be banded on the left thumb and males on the right thumb. However, flying-fox thumbs are prone to damage or loss under certain conditions. For this reason, two of the study group were banded on the 'wrong' side. LBW (Left Banded Wing), an unsociable male, was essentially a left-sider but, as mentioned earlier, was often found in the small lower triangle of the roof, away from the others, or at times in one of the palms.

BRWF (Band Right Wing Female), who rejoined the group from the off-exhibit area a few days after the study began, added to my initial difficulties by keeping herself very much to herself, so that I seldom saw her properly unwrapped. The odd flash of banded thumb made me suspect she was a very small male, but the flashes were too brief for me to see that the tip of her left thumb was missing (making it impossible to band), let alone see any of the other relevant bits of her anatomy. Of all the flying-foxes, this small, dark female, with her unusually rich, dark auburn mantle was the one most closely bound to her small territory. BRW2 usually roosted within a metre or so of BRWF's territory, although at first there was little interaction that I could see. Their relationship later became a source of great interest.

When mating time arrived, I discovered that 010B was the centre of BRW2's attention, which led me to wonder how much this had to do with her generally relaxed and assured style. The German zoologist Gerhard Neuweiler found in his study of Indian flying-foxes (*Pteropus giganteus giganteus*) that the highest ranking animal in the group was always a male and seemed to be governed by age and strength. He also noted that, during mating season, the females were ranked according to the status of their mate. BRW2 was not the oldest of the males, but he certainly appeared to be the largest and strongest, and over the following years 010B remained his preferred mate. (Not that he wouldn't look elsewhere on those occasions when she refused to accommodate him.) We shall return anon to the implications of a possible mate- or parent-related rank.

The situation on the left side of the cage was less clear cut. Apart from LBW, there was the fully grown but quite young Pale, a light-coloured male almost identical in appearance to the females Spot and Fang. Although he was not by any means weedy as far as physique went, he seemed to defer to other bats, regardless of sex or size. Split, a mature male, was something of a wanderer. He was easily identified by his ear, which had somehow been torn from base to tip.

The flying-fox most likely to be the dominant male on the left side was an ancient who became known as Scruff. A dirty old bat, he could no longer fly due to badly healed wing fractures, and his fur was frequently decorated with bits of leftover dinner. His tatty, scarred ears were set on a massive blunt wedge of a head. He was probably rising 19 or 20 years old. Nevertheless, he may well have been the sire of 010's offspring. By the time mating season arrived it occurred to me that he was holding his position by default — but more of that later. What is of interest at this juncture is that 010 was his preferred mate, but only by a narrow margin. Scruff also formed a strange out-of-season relationship with HW (later to be known as Endora) for a time and, during the mating season, attempted to distribute his favours among 010, Spot, Fang and Endora.

The second day following my return to the Healesville flying-foxes was warm and sunny, with the slightest of breezes sharpening the air from time to time. The bats stretched their wings, reshuffling them before returning to sleep, or snuffling through sun-warmed fur as they groomed themselves. 001, the first baby, now eight-and-a-half weeks old, scrambled out of its mother's leathery embrace to clamber around the roof on its own. 001B, now fully furred, hung beside its mother, reaching across to suckle from the nipple in her exposed armpit as she basked. Of course I had no way of knowing whether this one had been doing so at an earlier date. However, this more or less corresponded to the situation in the wild, where the youngster would be able to survive the night apart from its mother, left with others in a 'crèche' tree until shortly before dawn.

After the night's foraging, flying-fox mothers return to the nursery area, flying around the tree and uttering calls. The youngsters also begin calling. The female then makes a landing near a baby, sniffing it to establish its identity as her own. She is not always right first time and will push an unrelated youngster away from her. Arriving at her own offspring, she exposes her chest and grooms the little one as it climbs aboard. John Nelson's laboratory investigations showed that three-week-old babies will board the next best female, whether or not it is their mother. The females recognised their own young by smell, even when they were was concealed in a cloth bag. (Nelson, J. E., 1965.)

I had given very little thought to the matter of whether or not flying-foxes distinguished between individual humans. Although they did usually react restlessly to keepers in uniform (and bus drivers wearing similar uniforms) the traffic of general public through the enclosure seldom upset them. The animals seemed unconcerned by my presence below their roost after the first few days, even though I was dressed differently each time. Before long the noises made by my shuffling a bag of equipment on the gravel or juggling bits of camera also went unremarked. Presumably I had been relegated to the status of harmless 'furniture' in the cage, in much the same way that they disregarded the wild wedge-tailed eagles that circled overhead or perched high over the cage in a eucalypt, or the racket of the dingoes next door sorting out some dispute or other. The noise of machinery or passing service vehicles, however, sent the bats scattering around the roof, loping along slung from thumbs and feet. These noises apparently did not belong to the flying-foxes' aural wallpaper — they were not sufficiently familiar to be judged non-threatening.

Thus I was surprised when I walked into the cage late one hot morning to see the bats panic and flee in all directions from my approach. Then I realised what was different — I was wearing a large sun hat. I left the enclosure, let the bats settle and returned sans hat. Not so much as an eyebrow was raised. Before long, however, the hat became accepted as part of me for the rest of that summer. At its first appearance the following year, the initial reaction was once again panic.

As we have already seen, vision and, to a lesser extent, hearing, are important senses in the life of a megachiropteran. The information from both of these sense organs is processed in the midbrain, or mesencephalon, a thick-walled section with a small central cavity.

The significance of hearing to flying-foxes is different to that in microbats. It is used primarily in association with communication or social activity and in registering the approach of potential predators. Calford and McAnally (1986) reported on the auditory centres in the brain and the range of sound frequencies heard by little red and grey-headed flying-foxes.

The nucleus of the auditory or sound processing pathway in the midbrain is known as the inferior colliculus. It is located next to the much larger visual nucleus or superior colliculus. Examination showed that the auditory centre in the little red and grey-headed flying-foxes is surprisingly small, between 10% and 20% of the little red's body weight. This ratio is comparable to a mouse.

Although popular opinion presumes that bats generally are able to hear sounds in the very high frequency range inaudible to most adult humans, this is not the case with the little red or grey-headed flying-foxes. In 1980 Heffner and Heffner presented evidence that the limitation of an animal's ability to hear sounds in the higher range of frequencies is inversely related to the size of the head. The flying-foxes' upper limit was established experimentally as being only slightly lower than

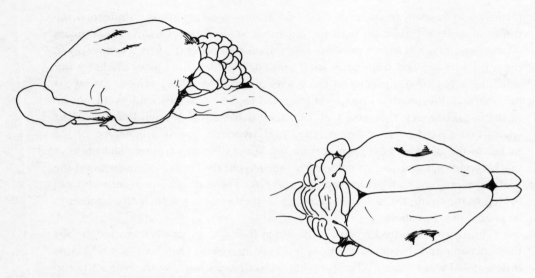

The brain of the grey-headed flying-fox (*Pteropus poliocephalus*).

predicted for their head widths of 40 millimetres (little red) and 45 millimetres (grey-headed). For the little red flying-fox, the optimum sound sensitivity was around 11 kilohertz, dropping off markedly above 40 kilohertz and (surprisingly) below 2 kilohertz. The upper limit was 50 kilohertz (at 60 decibels SPL).

John Nelson's research (1963) into vocal communication in flying-foxes showed that, for the greater part, the animals' vocalisations had maximum energy in the range between 4 kilohertz and 6 kilohertz. Although it is outside their optimum sensitivity range, vocalisations within this range will carry further than the higher frequencies, which would be more inclined to be reflected by small obstacles. Obviously this is a more practical arrangement when the animals' lifestyle and habitat are taken into consideration.

To return to the question of 'primate-likeness', Calford and McAnally compared audiograms from members of the Megachiroptera with those of Primates. As shown above, the flying-foxes showed very poor sensitivity to the low frequency range of sounds. The higher primates — the apes — showed extremely good sensitivity in the low frequency range, while at the other end of the primate order, the prosimians (lemurs and galagos or 'bushbabies') were reasonably sensitive in that range. The Senegal galago is comparable in head size to the grey-headed flying-fox and shows the expected similarity in upper limit and optimum sensitivity frequency. However, its hearing in the lower frequency range is better than that of the flying-fox.

Although the microbats share the poor sensitivity to low frequency sound, their systems for hearing are far more specialised and prominent than those seen in *Pteropus*. John Nelson and Heinz Stephan (1981) concluded from their comparative work on the brains of Australian bats that the pteropodids examined (*Pteropus* and *Nyctimene*) had more highly developed brains than any of the other groups.

There is a marked contrast between the mega- and microbats in the degree to which their vision is developed. For microbats, it plays only a minor role when compared to hearing and sense of smell. Megabats have eyes specially adapted for low light vision, but are still able to see well in daylight. Stand in a flying-fox cage or camp for a while and you will see for yourself. Although the pteropid eye is not quite as efficient as the human version in bright light, it performs far better than ours in the dimly lit hours of its peak feeding and flying activity.

Graydon and his fellow researchers (1986) compare flying-fox vision to that of a cat. Most of us have seen the extremes of contraction and expansion of a cat's pupil as the light conditions change. Although flying-foxes have a round, rather than vertical pupil, you will notice that in good light it contracts to almost pinhead size, expanding dramatically as the light decreases.

The ability to vary the size of the pupil so widely is not the only way in which the flying-fox eye is adapted — it controls the amount of light entering the eye, but once the light is admitted it must be transmitted to the appropriate centre within the brain in order to process the visual information it transmits (see above).

The typical mammalian eye — including ours — is lined, except at the front, by the retina. The outer layer of the eye is pigmented (the choroid, which contains blood vessels); an inner transparent layer contains nerve cells and receptors, 'rods' and 'cones'. The rods are sensitive to very dim light and the cones are concerned with discriminating fine detail and colour. Flying-foxes have almost entirely rod vision. Between these receptor cells in the inner layer are intermediary nerve cells, which connect the visual receptors to the optic nerves that leave the eye, nerve fibres, and glia (the supporting tissue in the central nervous systems of vertebrates). Behind all this is the stalk-like optic nerve, connecting the eye to the brain.

In flying-foxes, the choroid — the layer immediately behind or outside the retina — is studded with thickenings or papillae. (This heavily pigmented layer may be compared to the black box of a camera in as much as it reduces light reflection.) The contours of the retina in turn follow the form of these projections, much in the way that kitchen foil lining a fancy cake tin will follow the pattern of bumps or ridges. Flying-foxes also have a relatively thick retina, but unlike those of similar thickness in other animals it is not vascularised or penetrated by blood vessels. Even though the papillae penetrate almost into the innermost cell layer of the retina, the blood vessels within them are sheathed from it by the layer of pigment cells. Think of poking your finger into a slab of clay several centimetres thick; the inner contour follows your finger whilst the opposite surface remains flat, and the blood within the finger is separated from the clay by your skin.

A number of functions have been suggested for this arrangement within the flying-fox eye. Perhaps the most likely is connected with the supply of oxygen to the inner layer of the retina. The hexagonally arranged papillae are spaced from each other in such a way that oxygen is able to diffuse into the area of the retina not supplied with blood vessels. The walls of the blood vessels within the papillae appear to be more permeable than those of the underlying vessels. So, at this point, forget the finger in the clay metaphor, it has served its purpose.

Further evidence is to be found in the structure of the pigment cells layer. When catching the eye of an animal in the beam of a torch or headlights at night, you will notice a characteristic 'eyeshine' — sometimes yellowish-green, sometimes red. Eyeshine is usually the result of light reflecting from the tapetum. In flying-foxes the cells of the pigment layer covering the papillae are thinner and have fewer granules of pigment than in other areas. However, amongst the granules of pigment are other highly refractile granules. These, rather than the more conventional tapetum, are thought to cause eyeshine. Neuweiler (1962) and Pirie (1966) propose that this flying-fox version of the tapetum provides the least opposition to diffusion of oxygen. (Graydon et al. 1986.)

So, what goes on beyond the retina? Flying-foxes, like primates, have binocular vision. There is, as mentioned, a pathway between retina and midbrain, but it differs from that of animals not belonging to the Primates or Megachiroptera. This pathway is linked to only a very small part of one retina, not the entire retina as in some other mammals. Although this pathway is so much reduced, there is another pathway for transmission of information from eye to brain. This greatly enlarged brain feature is known as the geniculostriate system. These are the characteristics discovered, to his surprise, by Jack Pettigrew, when he examined the brain of a grey-headed flying-fox. Further investigations revealed that the microchiropterans do not rejoice in the same arrangement of their equipment. Thus began the great systematic debate. (Pettigrew, 1986.)

I thought for a moment, back in 1988, that Pettigrew had penetrated further into the public mind than expected, when an American visitor with two compatriots in tow marched into the flying-fox cage at Healesville Sanctuary. The smartly dressed young woman cast a businesslike eye over the aviary, dismissing the catbirds and kingfishers, and fixed on the flying-foxes. She then began a brisk lecture to her less erudite companions: 'Of course these things aren't really bats you know.' I waited for a pronouncement on primate origins. She continued: 'In fact they're not birds at all — they're rodents.' Well, that, as they say, 'learned' me!

The flying-foxes' introduction to what they seemed to regard as my dubious taste in millinery happened two days before Christmas. As the day grew warmer I removed the offending hat, parking it on top of my equipment bag, and moved to stand out of the sun under a small scrubby tree in the left corner of the cage. Before long I was joined by the female, HW, who had shown such interest in 001's birth two months before. I had, in the meantime, discovered that her 'house' name was Endora. She scrambled rather inelegantly from the roof into the spindly top branches of the tree and down to a position where she could rake her thumb claws gently through my hair. As I moved around under the tree, she followed, pulling rather harder at my plait when I resisted her overtures.

It is difficult to ignore a determined flying-fox and my resistance, in the name of proper objectivity was, in the long run, not bat-proof. Besides, there is something essentially flattering about being not only accepted, but approached, by a 'wild' animal — even if it is in captivity. I justified the indulgence of playing with her by examining her thoroughly for distinguishing

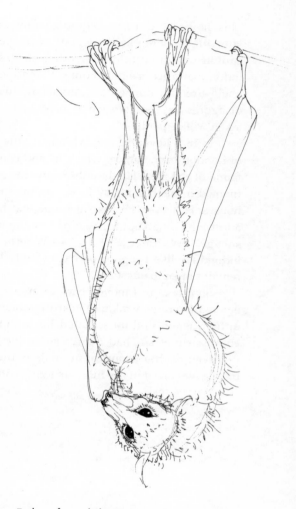

Endora, formerly known as HW.

marks. After rubbing her belly and scratching her back to her satisfaction, I allowed her to examine my watch and jewellery. Everything had been inspected with claws, teeth and tongue from every possible angle before I decided that I should be concentrating on the activities overhead.

When, with the help of Dr Dedee Woodside, I eventually obtained copies of the Taronga Zoo, Sydney, records giving me more detail on the early lives of some of the bats, I found that quite a number of them had been hand-reared.

This, however, did not seem to guarantee that the animals would remain tame in later life — some keeping staff have the scars to prove it. When the group is caught up for weighing or other checks, there is quite wide variation in the individual reactions to handling. Some, even though raised by their mothers in the enclosure and unused to humans at close quarters, show little sign of distress or aggression. Some, such as BRW2 and Fang, make it quite clear that liberties taken will be paid for.

In 1874 Reverend S. J. Whitmee wrote to the Secretary of the Zoological Society of London from Samoa, where he had contributed a great deal to the study of the fauna of the area. He described how the Samoans tamed specimens of *P. whitmeei* (named in his honour by E. R. Alston) and that the tame animals never left their houses. However, he described one that he reared from a 'youthful stage' and an adult which he kept for two or three months as remaining very shy and 'rather savage'. (Whitmee, S. J., 1874.) Whether Whitmee happened upon a stroppy individual, like Fang, or perhaps simply lacked the right touch with flying-foxes, remains open to question.

Shortly after I moved back to my usual roost on a log, out of reach, a visitor entered the cage, walking toward Endora's tree. It was difficult not to feel slightly miffed, when Endora solicited his attention with just as much confidence and enthusiasm as she had mine. One of the great pitfalls of becoming so intimately involved with a group of animals is the temptation to imagine that they feel themselves on similarly intimate terms with us as individuals.

010 with Roger in the foreground, and 010B with Lucy.

Goannas prey on fallen baby flying-foxes, helping keep the camp clean.

Hand-rearing
Orphans

I have already mentioned Helen Luckhoff as one of the organisers of the 'Batty Boat Trips' on the Brisbane River. My first meeting with Helen was memorable on a number of levels, from the first experience of being surrounded by tame flying-foxes, exploring me with as much excited curiosity as I examined them, to the sheer force of Helen's personality, a mixture of generosity, hilarity and absolute tenacity. I had already been introduced to a plethora of myths, legends and 'Helen stories', well before visiting her at her home, which doubles as the headquarters of a voluntary network for rearing orphaned bats and other beasts.

I was taken to visit Helen by a friend from the University of Queensland who had also been well-primed with stories of Helen sharing her bed with baby flying-foxes (individuals prone to be 'dawn screamers' as she terms them), and similar tales of her extraordinary devotion to duty. Perhaps my favourite memory of that day is the look on my friend's face when, following the arrival of a new orphan at the door, Helen returned to her seat, politely enquiring whether we minded her feeding it while we talked, and purposefully plunged a hand into her cleavage. When, after a brief rummage, the hand reappeared clutching nothing more than a small, rubber-teated bottle of milk, nicely warmed to serving temperature, my companion sagged with relief.

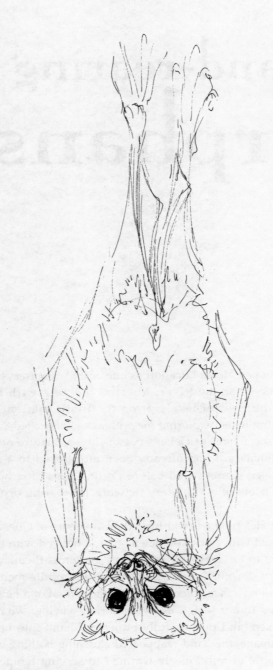

Grey-headed flying-fox (*Pteropus poliocephalus*).

Helen Luckhoff's association with flying-foxes began with Emily. In Jamboree Heights, a suburb of Brisbane, there is a tree favoured by flying-foxes as a feeding site. There are eight electric wires running between its branches. It was here that Emily was found clinging to the corpse of her electrocuted mother. For the next two weeks her rescuers did their best for her until holiday plans forced them to pass her on to the local vet. In spite of their care she was severely malnourished. That same afternoon the vet called for expert advice from Les Hall.

As it happened, that was also the day that Helen Luckhoff came to the surgery, bringing a much-loved cat for help in its last hours. Years before, Helen had lived in Zimbabwe and South Africa, where she had hand-raised orphaned wild animals from time to time. Seeing Emily — at that stage still dubbed Harry — Helen asked for a chance to rear the unprepossessing waif. At first the vet refused. However, some hours later, when it became clear that euthanasia was all that could be suggested for her ageing cat, Helen was offered consolation in the form of a challenge — she was to rear Emily.

When she joined the Luckhoff household, Emily was probably somewhere between four and six weeks old and weighed a mere 100 grams — as we now know, very little for her age. Her previous minders had tried a diet of 5 millilitres of a mixture of skim milk and water at four-hourly intervals. This was apparently inadequate. After some experimentation, Helen lit upon a commercially prepared milk formula for infants. The result was a bat free of stomach trouble and producing smaller, more normal, faeces. Ultimately, an ideal rearing formula was found by trial and error over a period of 12 months, trying ten variations on ten orphaned flying-foxes.

In spite of her traumatic launch in life, Emily proved to be a friendly little animal, seeming quite content to be carried around, wrapped in cloth, on Helen's comfortable chest. With the curiosity and fondness for contact typical of her species, Emily grew up apparently hellbent on participation in family life. She spent hours happily hooked to the wool holder of the knitting machine, or dangling from the music stand of the electric organ while Helen played.

A month or so after Emily's arrival, Boris, a black flying-fox, was introduced to the household. Bald and broken, toothless, and minus the tips of his ears, Boris gave every evidence of being led by old age to death's door. He was cleaned up by the vet and brought home by Helen to die in peace and comfort. As it happened, Boris took a liking to peace and comfort and lived on to deflower Emily a year later.

Boris was to prove useful in the designing of diets for hand-reared youngsters as they passed the weaning stage. Being wild-caught, he rejected unsuitable offerings, which might otherwise have been taken by the younger bats.

Elizabeth, the product of Boris's new lease of life, stayed with her mother, although Emily's subsequent offspring became independent in the usual manner. Each year, before Emily gave birth, Elizabeth would resume suckling like an infant, just as I had observed SM doing with 010B at Healesville. This continued until 1988, when Elizabeth, a hybrid and thus supposedly sterile, brazenly defied science and gave birth to a youngster of her own.

Beside the Luckhoff house stands a huge Moreton Bay fig tree, which produces up to three crops a year. It has long been used by the wild flying-foxes as a feeding and nursery tree. At six months of age, on a regular training flight around the back yard, Emily flew the coop. She met up with the visiting bats and disappeared into the wild. Three days passed before she at last swooped back through the kitchen door, landing on the knitting machine. She was well, but thirsty, apparently not having mastered the technique of skimming over water to drink on the wing. The one lasting reminder of her elopement was a damaged wing — its span being wider than the kitchen door through which she had returned.

Her injury has meant that Emily is one of the exceptions to Helen's policy of returning orphans to life in the wild. However, she and the small group of incapacitated flying-foxes who remain permanently in the Luckhoff menagerie play an important part in the rearing and rehabilitation of others. Emily was the catalyst for the development of a larger rearing programme and, as time went on, further study into a number of aspects of flying-fox biology. There has been close cooperation throughout between Helen, Les Hall, Len Martin and others from the University of Queensland.

When orphaned infants arrive at Helen's they usually weigh somewhere between 49 and 85 grams, the former being well below normal birthweight. They are fed as soon as possible, as many are dehydrated and starved as a result of clinging for some time to a dead mother, or lying about, having fallen from their mother, before being rescued. (Observations in the wild suggest that it is not usual for the female to retrieve a fallen baby. Looking at the situation of most camps it is easy to see why the attempt would be fruitless and a danger to the mother's survival. She would have difficulty taking off from the ground or the tangled understorey and would thus be vulnerable to predators.) They are fed slightly warmed milk formula, using a teat with a 4-millimetre diameter. At first, the infants are fed on demand, usually between 3 and 5 millilitres at each session. After this the feeding must continue at two- to four-hourly intervals and the infants must also be cleaned regularly with baby lotion. A great deal of a mother flying-fox's time during the first few weeks is spent grooming her offspring. Although the task is not one for dilettantes, there seems to be no shortage of volunteers in Helen's small army of bat-rearers.

By the time they are six or eight weeks old, the youngsters should be capable of hanging by their feet. They are then transferred to a wire cage furnished with a heating pad on one wall and a folded towel on the floor. Most will use the towel as a support for their head and shoulders when sleeping. The youngsters are kept caged for their own protection; otherwise they are apt to wander and could, in the spirit of enquiry, land themselves in trouble. Emily once disappeared, only to be discovered under a bed.

At this age most wild youngsters would be old hands at being left 'parked' in a nursery tree, often in the outer area of the camp, where there is more foliage. The group of youngsters is not left entirely to its own devices, as some observers report seeing adults flying in and out of the crèche throughout the night. From the age of about four weeks, the young can not only manage to hang by their feet alone, but, perhaps more importantly for parking purposes, they are fully furred. They are able to thermoregulate — control their body temperature — efficiently enough to survive without the mother's body reducing heat loss and transferring warmth to them.

The lifestyle of flying-foxes exposes them to an extraordinary range of climatic factors within which they must somehow maintain body temperature and metabolic rate within a sufficiently limited range for their survival. In the tree top roosts open to sun, rain and wind, they may be subjected to extremes of heat and cold. Nocturnal foraging flights may cover many kilometres, burning up hard-won energy. They are comparatively small animals, which means that their surface area to volume ratio is high (the larger the animal, the lower the ratio) and added to this are the wing membranes. This would seem, at first, to increase their lack of resistance to external temperature factors.

Research into the ways that flying-foxes deal with these basic problems was carried out by Bartholomew, Leitner and Nelson in the early 1960s. They worked with grey-headed and little red flying-foxes and also, to a lesser extent, with *Syconycteris*, the tiny Queensland blossom bats.

They found, amongst other things, that the pteropids they investigated seemed to have slower resting heart rates than other mammals of similar size. If the same is true during acitivity, it could be of great advantage to the flying-foxes in terms of reducing the load on the heart during the long-distance flights they often undertake.

In the laboratory, they were able to measure the effects of temperature on heart rate and found that it varied. From a mean minimum of 128 beats per minute, when the ambient temperature was 30 degrees Celsius, the rate increased in conditions of both higher and lower temperature, reaching 266 beats per minute at 5 degrees Celsius.

The research also showed that grey-headed flying-foxes are able to maintain their core temperature at around 35 to 39 degrees Celsius (normal for most mammals) in surroundings where the temperature ranges between 5 and 40 degrees Celsius. There are a number of ways in which the animals can influence their body temperature in the face of rising or falling ambient temperatures. If the surrounding air is cooled rapidly, the bats begin to shiver (as we do, often without thinking of the reason). This activity quickly raises the body temperature by about one degree Celsius and maintains it there for as long as the shivering continues.

One degree may not seem much help, considering the apparently (in this situation) maladapted wings, which would seem in their naked state to be a further source of heat loss. Indeed, when wrapped around the flying-fox's body, the area of membrane exposed drops in temperature to within two or three degrees of that of the surrounding air. However, in this wing-wrapped position, much of the membrane is unexposed and there is, in effect, a double layer of insulation trapping air between the bat's body and the outside. In the experiments with captive animals, the layer of air between the body and the wing was found to be at least ten degrees warmer than the outside temperature.

When the temperature is raised above 40 degrees Celsius, the wings once again combine with other mechanisms to cool the animal. Under experimental conditions, grey-headed flying-foxes began panting, open-mouthed, as the temperature neared 40 degrees, increasing their breathing rate from an average of 33 breaths per minute in temperatures up to 25 degrees Celsius, to 200 or more breaths per minute. They also began salivating and licking the areas around their muzzles, wrists, thumbs, chests, and the wing membranes. The movement of the wings assists in temperature regulation by moving cooling air across the engorged blood vessels of the wings and those of the interfemoral membranes attached to the inner sides of the legs. The thin, naked ears also contain blood vessels which dilate to allow heat loss.

Similar evaporative cooling systems are seen in other animals, such as the pelican with its great pouch of loose skin below the beak. Kangaroos use a similar but less dramatic method — watch them on hot days, licking the underside of their wrists.

Bats' are unusual in their arrangement of dual systems of blood vessels. In one network of vessels, large arteries conduct blood from the heart through smaller arteries, into fine capillaries, then through small veins into larger veins, returning it to the animal's heart. Linked to this supply and removal system is the thermoregulatory one in the wings, consisting of small arteries connected to small veins, without the usual mammalian arrangement of capillaries in between. The lack of an intermediate network of capillaries means that there is no drop in pressure as the blood passes through the wing's cooling system. (Bartholomew, Leitner and Nelson, J. E., 1964.)

Bartholomew and company found that adult animals could keep their body temperature around one degree lower than the ambient temperature for at least an hour by these means. In other words, they were still able to function within the normal 35 to 39 degrees Celsius core temperature range. The little red flying-foxes differed slightly from the grey-headed flying-foxes in that they tolerated high temperatures slightly more easily, allowing their body temperatures to rise to 40 or 41 degrees Celsius, before resorting to the same cooling strategies as the grey-headed flying-foxes. Little red flying-foxes are, however, less able to cope with low temperatures than the other species. Their strange clustering in the roost could be a way of combating heat loss while resting.

The infant grey-headed flying-foxes have a body temperature of around 34 to 37 degrees Celsius. From as early as two days of age they are able to maintain some difference between their body temperature and that of the surrounding air when off their mother for a number of hours. However, they do lose heat much more rapidly than when on the mother's body. This rate of cooling decreases as the youngster becomes older, and by the age of 15 to 17 days the shivering response becomes apparent. (Human babies also take some time to develop this anti-cooling response.) By the time the flying-foxes are four weeks old, as we have already seen, they are fully furred, and are able to maintain their body temperature at an adult level in a surrounding temperature of 10 degrees. This corresponds quite well with the conditions they are likely to need to cope with in the wild.

Interestingly, the little red flying-fox, a species more likely to be plagued by extremes of heat and better adapted to it than the grey-headed flying-fox, gives birth to its young in autumn, rather than spring.

For Helen, this means that the problems of orphan-rearing are not neatly restricted to a few months of the year. One of the critical periods in a young animal's life is weaning — making the transition from mother's milk to an adult diet. In captivity I have seen this occurring anywhere between four and six months after birth. The records from elsewhere are similar. Some mothers seem more reluctant than others to allow prolonged suckling and it is a pathetic sight to see a harassed female hotly and persistently pursued by a large youngster, energetically attempting to wrestle its way between her wings each time she stops to draw breath. This is what has repeatedly occurred with 010B and her late weaners.

In the Healesville study group I have often watched youngsters of weaning age exploring the mouths of their mothers. With the orphans it is time to begin weaning them onto a fruit diet when the young animals begin exploring the feeder's mouth while eating. They are not allowed to eat fruit until they are able to hang independently. At this time they also begin to lap milk, rather than needing the teat. As they change to adult food, the milk is gradually rejected. However, drinking water must still be provided.

It is also time for development of the flying muscles, and the small flying-foxes wing-flap vigorously while holding the wire with their feet. This can be hazardous, as the wing bones can be damaged if the space is too small, so exercise outside the confines of the cage is essential. The orphans are kept inside until they are able to fly well — usually by February.

Now three or four months old, they are provided with a warm, protected sleeping area, adjacent to that of the adults. At this point they are ready to begin the integration process. After a couple of days, the door dividing the two halves of the enclosure is opened and the groups are able to mingle.

When they are at last mixed with the adult bats, the juveniles must learn about things like territoriality and submission to the older bats. Groups of youngsters are introduced to the captive adults on Saturdays, when they can be supervised. Their first reaction is fright, but most settle within 24 hours. Some youngsters, notably those who lacked human company during rearing, will go to the bottom of the cage and may refuse to come up, even for food. This can last from a few days to a fortnight or two months, depending on the circumstances of their raising. Some are cocky with the adults from a very early stage — these are rebuffed vocally. The relationship between altitude and rank within the group is mentioned by Neuweiler in his study of Indian flying-foxes. He refers to the dominant males commandeering the highest and best shaded positions in his captive study group. (Neuweiler, 1969.)

In the course of teaching flying-fox etiquette, the adults may chase the juveniles, but they do not actually harm them. When Annabel, a little red flying-fox, was introduced to the adults, Emily wrapped her in her wings during the cold weather, until the little red learned to roost back to back with her for warmth.

Flying practice chez Luckhoff is conducted in darkness at about seven o'clock at night. There are two very high trees behind the cage, which serve as landmarks for the bats, which return to the trees and then to Helen. As reinforcements to these landmarks, a red bucket is placed on the roof of the cage, which also has white stripes painted on it. In spite of this, some young bats still get bushed and have to be returned by neighbours. One youngster arrived at a neighbour's barbecue after an evening out. Helen was duly summoned and eventually marched back along the street with the errant bat flying ahead of her.

In the second year of Helen's programme, three orphans were reared. Subsequently between eight and 12 were reared in a season, with the help of 'foster parents'. It was then possible to release them as a 'squadron'. They began integrating without pressure, but some took two or three years to assimilate completely. Now new ones are able to go 'from kindergarten to high school' with the older releases.

During March and April the young animals are ready to be released. They are free to return to the back yard feeding station, but gradually their dependence on it lessens, showing that they are learning to forage. They may fly to join the nearby Indooroopilly colony, returning intermittently until the camp migrates for the winter.

If a youngster returns in poor condition from time spent out with wild flying-foxes, it is usually due to the lack of 'godparent' protection from older bats. The older releases can become overworked in a season when too many orphans are released for integration. This occurred when the six resident godparents were swamped with youngsters in a year when the wild food supply was unreliable. The other adult bats coming through were jumpy and not interested in the young.

A few of the orphans return to Helen for their first winter and a number of tame flying-foxes return year after year. There may be up to 90 bats dining with the Luckhoffs on any one night. Those remaining in captivity receive at least three varieties of soft fruits, along with full cream milk powder or Glaxo Complan (1 to 2 teaspoons per animal). In the colder weather avocadoes, butter or olive oil are also added to their diet once a week. When available, native blossoms and mulberry leaves are included with the fruit. Add the collecting of foodstuffs to the task of chopping, mixing and serving, and daily meals become quite an event.

The reserves of energy and determination needed to do this kind of hands-on bat work, to coordinate a network of people from vastly different walks of life prepared to rear orphaned wild animals, and to participate in the work of various researchers and wildlife preservation groups are enormous. Beside this, Helen Luckhoff has managed to rear her own family and cope with a full-time job — and still knows how to laugh! I take my hat off to her.

CHAPTER 7

Of Wings and Thumbs

The opening days of 1989 brought further progress in the painstaking process of identifying individuals within the Healesville flying-fox group. By this stage I often 'knew' which bat I was looking at — probably a combination of roosting location and unconsciously absorbed details of posture, attitude and overall body shape. But without being able to justify precisely why I thought which was which, I was unwilling to make statements about who was doing what and to whom. It can be frustratingly difficult to pick small positive marks of identity in a group of fast-moving animals. It was still some time before my eye automatically went to the critical bit of bat, such as an ear or a missing thumb tip, without being distracted from the action. However, like coming to grips with a foreign language, as long as things moved slowly I could keep abreast of events and individuals.

The second day of January was hot and still. When I arrived at eleven-thirty that morning, the bats had not yet commenced the usual hot-day exodus from the apex and top quadrants to the lower shaded area of the roof. Most hung open, suspended by various combinations of toes and thumbs, languidly fanning themselves with a wing. For the first time, I saw 010 move away from her youngster. She briefly moved over to where another female (Spot, I think) was

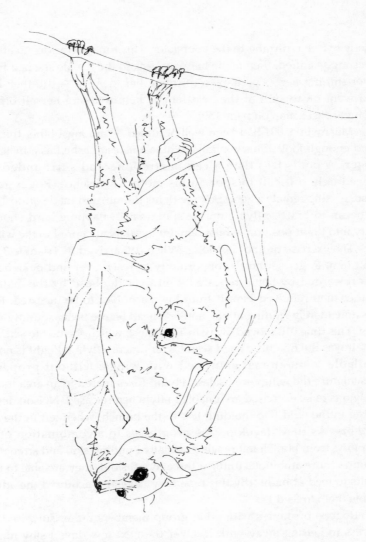

Grey-headed flying-fox (*Pteropus poliocephalus*) with young.

hanging, then returned to her offspring for a bout of vigorous mutual grooming. Previously it had been 001 who did the adventuring, returning to the security of 010's chest when alarmed. Up to this point, she had remained a far more clinging mother than 010B. At two-and-a-half months, her youngster was still some time away from weaning, but its independence was rapidly increasing and its social confidence was already obvious.

Before long, 010 was on the move again, climbing up toward the centre ridge briefly before returning to the youngster. This time there was no attempt to groom, she simply sniffed, then made her way back to the female she had first approached. After sniffing her — perhaps confirming her identity — 010 then bypassed Scruff and went on to sniff at the next female before taking herself off to roost in the Triangle 3 (see map on page 159).

Meanwhile, 001 had been well occupied — amongst other things, giving me a good enough look at his genitalia to at last be established as a male and christened Roger. A penis less than a centimetre long and surrounded by fur can be exceedingly difficult to spot. In his mother's absence, Roger gave the nearest unsuspecting female a good poke with his thumb, and made off to Triangle 3 where he began to practise flying on the spot, that is, flapping hard enough to raise his body into flight position, whilst remaining safely anchored to the wire by his toes.

The exercise did not last long. When 010 arrived in Triangle 3 to roost not far from him, Roger seized the opportunity to reach over and poke her. This time he was rewarded by being repeatedly hit over the head by the maternal wrist; his mother then removed herself from his reach. Not to be deterred, Roger followed, this time merely sniffing at his mother's head before being soundly walloped on his own. This time 010 moved away to Triangle 2, which seemed to settle the matter.

It was the first time I had seen Roger practise flying. Flight is not automatically available to an animal equipped with wings; without properly developed musculature the wings are useless. Flying-foxes reared in an area too small to allow the wings to be exercised are unable to fly when released. Nelson describes how the young in the wild flap, holding fast to the branch, when left in the crèche by their mothers. As they develop, this progresses to a combination of flapping and dropping from branch to branch, gradually building skill and strength. The training becomes more ambitious until, at three months old, they are able to fly out with the adults to feed at night. (By this time they have also acquired the adult dentition to enable them to feed.)

Roger's pushiness with other group members rather surprised me, as did his success in getting away with it. Over the next few days I saw him hooking and hitting out at LBW male and another adult bat without any visible sign of retaliation. The former simply ignored him and the latter just continued on its way past him. He was still spending time suckling and in mutual grooming with his mother. I wondered whether there is a general tolerance of youngsters in flying-fox society, from which Roger would cease to benefit as he matured. It remained to be seen how 001B would fare with the adults by comparison.

By the end of its first month, 001B was spending more time hanging by its own feet while suckling and had begun to make brief independent sorties around its mother's roosting area. 001B also became involved in social contacts.

On a brassy, bright day with the temperature in the low thirties, tempered occasionally by the suggestion of a breeze, the bats were fanning and fidgeting. Roger tried hitting a passing adult before clambering onto his approaching mother. He still hung by his own feet, pressed close to her belly, but not suckling. Some distance away old Scruff was sneezing and spluttering small rainbow mists of mucus. He was a juicy old codger and often did this. Endora was down in the small corner tree, too busy socialising with human visitors to concern herself with other bats. Over in Triangle 3, 010B, with 001B on board, was involved in a brief exchange of squawks and thumb-sparring with the pale-headed female roosting nearby. Peace restored, 010B hung with wings open, showing her offspring, restless against her chest and not suckling. The little one looked across at the pale-headed female and reached out to touch her. This was not well received; the female assumed an aggressive posture, and 010B and 001B moved away to their more often used area in the quadrants.

I was left wondering about the reason for their retreat — was it purely a matter of territory, or simply that flying-foxes have days when they cannot be bothered standing their ground. 010B was a big strong female and, in mating season, consort of the dominant male in that area. Did distance from the dominant male have any bearing on it? I was later to see BRW defend BRWF and her offspring, sired by him. Because of the difficulty of identifying individuals in those days, I am unwilling to trust the record sufficiently to state BRW2's position while the interaction was in progress.

On hot days such as that, there was usually a great deal of restlessness and slow milling about towards midday, as the bats congregated in the one shaded corner. However, although they were roosting in closer proximity to each other and territories were jumbled, there was little evidence of squabbling. Even BRW1 and LBW, whose usual territories included the outskirts of the shady area, showed little interest in the interlopers from other parts of the cage.

The flying-fox's thumbs are very useful and versatile implements, not simply part of the animal's flight equipment. They are used in defence for sparring and hooking, but also in initiating more amiable social contact and in manipulating food. It is in the latter capacity that the wing's evolution from a hand becomes strikingly obvious. The thumbs are also used like grappling hooks for climbing or hanging while the animal upends its body to relieve itself.

There are times when the bats can be so obliging in providing concise illustrations of a suite of behaviours or characteristics that I curse my lack of a video camera. This was the case on 12 January, when Endora, Roger and 010, with a few others as bit players, neatly summarised the functions of the pteropid thumb. The following extract from my notebook tells the story.

12.1.89: *Conditions mild, overcast, intermittent sun. Forecast maximum 19°C*

1540 *Endora still in tree; has been given half-eaten apple by visitor. Considerable visitor pressure in enclosure, therefore observations not constant on other bats.*

1544 *010B/001B intensive grooming.*

1545 *Endora still eating apple, held with right thumb and left foot.*

1546 *010/Roger wake, open, stretch, wing-wrap. 010B/Lucy hanging open. 010B hanging by two thumbs/one foot. 001B hanging by two feet.*

1547 *010B/001B shuffle position.*

1550 *010/Roger change position, closer to nearest bat. Endora returns to roof, centre Triangle 1, with apple in mouth. Resumes eating, holding apple with left foot.*

1551 *Split approaches 010B/001B — no reaction, even to body contact.*

1555 *010B pokes female to her left, then changes position.*

1556 *Lucy hanging separately but suckling.*

1559 *Cool breeze. 010B/001B wing-wrapped.*

1612 *Endora stuffs last of apple core into her mouth with left foot and changes position to Triangle 1 apex. Settles, wing-wrapped, eyes closed, still chewing.*

1615 *Endora finished eating — autogrooms wrists and thumbs.*

1617 *Endora approaches 010/Roger and pokes 010's wing. 010 opens, pokes Endora gently, no vocalisation. Roger urinates holding on to wire with one thumb and 010 with the other. Endora moves past BRW male (probably BRW1), who vocalises. Endora changes position to Quadrant 2 and autogrooms. 010/Roger groom.*

1621 *Roger leaves 010 and moves a few inches away, both autogroom and scratch.*

1622 *Endora finishes grooming and moves past BRW male (1?) — brief vocalisation/hooking. Endora returns to Triangle 1 near 010/Roger and autogrooms.*

1629 *Roger climbs around and onto front of 010 who is autogrooming. She accepts him, but is restless.*

1630 *Endora urinates, changes position past BRW male (1?) at a distance of +-30 cm. He vocalises, moves into Quadrant 1 and urinates.*

1631 *BRW male (1?) hooking at Endora. Endora retaliates and vocalises.*

1631·5 *Repeat above, but with BRW male sniffing Endora first.*

1632 *Roger off 010; approaches 010B, who is autogrooming and pokes her. 010B rebuffs and vocalises vigorously. BRW male (1?) repeats approach to Endora who gives vocal rebuff.*

General activity, changing positions and autogrooming.

1640 *BRW male hooking with both wings at Endora, who gives vocal rebuff. Both settle, wing-wrapped.*

1645 *010 and Roger hooking at and grooming each other. Endora urinates and defecates.*

1646 *Pale-ish, short-furred head female hooked at by BRW female and 010 — vocalisations, pale-ish female moves away. 010/Roger move away. Close.*

At this stage of the study you may note that the vocalisations are not described in detail. I later came to recognise not only a range of categories of vocalisation but also a range of 'deliveries', or manners, if you like. The volume and tone, or intensity, could be influenced not only by the stimulus or situation, but also by the social relationship between the individuals involved. We shall go into this a little later, when we get around to Scruff and Endora's strange little affair. For the time being it is worth bearing in mind that John Nelson identified a repertoire of 20 distinct vocalisations in his study of grey-headed flying-foxes.

We have diverged a little from the subject of wings and things pertaining to them. Remember *Pteropus* comes from the Greek for wing-footed. This refers to the fact that the flying-foxes' flight membrane is attached to the back of the second toe of the foot. To put the whole thing into human terms, imagine a membrane, the dactylopatagium, stretching across the back of your hand, to the tips of your fingers, closely linking a shortened index finger to the second finger, the thumb free. Extend that membrane from the side of the little finger down to the second toe and attached to its upper side, then imagine your legs and feet rotating until the knees bend backward and the toes can be curled forward. From the outer side of your ankle joint visualise a short, flexible spur of cartilage — this is the calcar and it supports a small, triangular auxiliary membrane (in some species of bat this is attached to the tail and is known as the uropatagium). From your shoulder to your thumb another membrane, the propatagium, is stretched, completing your flying outfit.

The wing membrane is not only controlled by the larger muscles of the chest and arms, but also by bundles of striated muscle tissue within the dermal layer (remember it is skin, made up of the outer dermis (epidermis) and the inner dermis) and elastic fibres. We have already looked at its blood supply in chapter 6. This vascular system is also located in the dermis.

I am constantly amazed at the strength and elasticity of flying-fox wings, as well as their powers of recovery. There was a time when the low-ranking male, Pale, had a tear in his wing that exposed nearly all of his finger bones where they met at the wrist joint, a hole probably 2 centimetres in diameter, which I expected to either remain open or heal in something of a mess. Today, there is virtually no sign that the tear ever occurred. Small holes frequently appear and seem to heal with little or no scarring in the bats in the study group. The wing membranes are indescribably soft to the touch, with a suggestion of velvet about them. Perhaps fine, extraordinarily pliable silk would be the nearest thing I could imagine. It always amuses me to watch the flying-foxes grooming their wings, making smooth masks of their faces and flicking tongues as they press them into the soft, fine skin.

As I mentioned earlier, the knees of bats operate in the opposite direction to ours and those of most mammals. This is one of a number of interesting structural adaptations for flight. Weight is an obvious problem for anything that is to become airborne. The greater the weight to be carried, the more energetically expensive flight becomes. Birds have a different approach to this problem; they have evolved light hollow bones. Interestingly, kiwis, which do not fly, have marrow-filled bones like mammals. The bats have lightened their structure by sacrificing strength and sturdiness in the lower body. Apart from, perhaps, vampire bats, which seem to bounce around quite efficiently on the ground, bats' leg bones are not strong enough to support the weight of their bodies in the standing position. Hanging is another matter; the upper body had to remain sufficiently sturdy to anchor flight muscles and operate the wings.

The hanging position is also a convenient one for launching into flight. Rather than an energy-expensive leap into the air, the bat simply releases its grip on the perch and drops into midair, flapping as it does so. The feet of bats are constructed in such a way that they do not have to exert conscious effort to 'hang on' to their roost in the way that we would have to grip a branch to support our suspended body weight. The ability of flying-foxes to hang safely for long periods, or even when asleep, often mystifies people. I recall one elderly lady visitor gazing up with a pained expression puckering her face, then turning to her companion to remark, 'Ooh, you'd think they'd get "arthuritis" hanging on to that wire all day!'. Actually, the grasp is maintained automatically, without muscular exertion, by the animal's body weight pulling on tendons in the feet, attached at the inner edge of the claws, which draw them down and forward into the gripping position.

Whilst we are on the subject of hanging, another question I often hear is, 'Why

Spot and Fang.

The blossom bat (*Macroglossus lagochilus*) extends a tongue longer than its head into the depths of blooms, seeking nectar.

doesn't all their blood run to their heads?', to which I usually respond, 'Why doesn't all the blood run to your feet?'. The answer in the case of the flying-foxes is not, as I once overheard a teacher explaining (in all seriousness) to a gaggle of curious youngsters, that they do not have enough blood for it to bother them! I was tempted to speculate on whether all his blood might indeed have run to his feet.

Bats generally have quite large hearts in proportion to their overall size, compared to other mammals. In the megachiropterans, the heart is rather elongated and located in the middle of the chest, tipped a little toward the left. Within the heart there are muscular valves which prevent the backward flow of the comparatively large stroke volume of blood, that is, the volume of blood pumped in each beat cycle. If the blood cannot flow backwards as it is pumped through the heart, it has to go forward through the system and go on circulating, regardless of which way is up. In bats this system is enhanced by the autonomous beating of the veins. We have already looked at the peculiarities of the wing's vascular system. As the veins within that system beat, it might be expected that some blood would be forced backwards into the arteries with each pulse. However, the veins, like the heart, are equipped with valves to prevent backflow. (Nelson, 1962.)

So, I suppose that more or less explains why flying-foxes don't faint when they turn head up to relieve themselves — just in case anyone was about to ask!

CHAPTER 8

The Mating Game

The third week of January 1989 brought the overture to the strange little affair played out by Endora and Scruff. It began on a cool, still day with a sky glowing pale, nacreous grey. The bats hung as still and quiet as the air as I crouched uncomfortably on my log, with little to distract me from the numbness insinuating its way through my inadequately upholstered hind parts. The numbness began to invade my mind, while my eyes remained fixed on the dark bundles of silence overhead. A flash of sunlight broke through the cloud and Roger was suddenly visible on the breast of 010. So quickly that I barely broke through my mental cloud in time to register it, he changed from her left to her right nipple and the maternal wings flicked back across to enshroud him. The only evidence of his presence was a third foot protruding from the tightly wrapped leathery parcel, clinging to the wire roof.

Forty-five minutes had passed since the beginning of the observation session before the cage suddenly filled with warm sunlight and activity. The flying-foxes shuffled their wings, stretching and grooming themselves and shuffling around their neighbours on the roof. Split and the unsociable male LBW left their roosting spots to wander, crossing paths as they did so. I was surprised to hear the 'chuckle' vocalisations that usually indicated tolerance between individuals, rather than the sharp quack-like 'squark' more often heard when the adults' paths crossed.

Five minutes later Scruff made his first approach to Endora — described in my notes as 'an attack?'. Whether or not aggression was involved, Endora wasn't having any, and rapidly climbed down into the corner sapling, where she entertained the visiting public for the ensuing 25 minutes. On returning to the roof, she encountered BRW1 and after a brief vocal exchange fled his approach by flapping down into the sapling, where a visitor offered the added incentive of a banana.

The bribing of bats, by the way, is definitely not a legitimate visitor activity. Like most modern zoos, the Sanctuary feeds its inhabitants a carefully designed and balanced diet. The offering of various dubious delicacies by the public is not only illegal, but often deleterious to the animals' health. In some cases, it is also a good way to get bitten.

For a minute or so BRW1 remained aloft, observing the benefits of corruption being demonstrated below, then he too climbed down into the branches, succumbing to the lure of a rapidly browning banana. Even when the illicit fruit had been withdrawn, the two bats remained in the sapling, socialising with their growing audience but, after half an hour with no more food forthcoming, Endora was ready to pack up her act. After three attempts to get past BRW1 in the branch above, she finally squawked and sparred her way through to the roof. He optimistically remained below.

This was the first time I had seen BRW1 behave in this way, soliciting food from humans, but before long he needed no lead from Endora to try his luck. In fact, he became even less inhibited than she was about the whole business. One morning, as I sat on my log eating a packet of chocolate pastilles for breakfast, my head was jerked back so sharply that I almost choked on the chunk I was chewing. Turning gingerly, for I was still being held by the hair, my eye came to rest, almost literally, on a dark furry snout. Moving quietly from his roost on the roof over my observation post, BRW1 had climbed down the vine-clad wall behind me and brazenly grabbed my plaited hair with a thumb claw to drag me — and the food — closer. We sat for a moment, staring at each other — or, in his case, gazing with the nearest to an ingratiating expression I have seen on a flying-fox, first at me, then pointedly at the chocolate. If flying-foxes were capable of disillusionment, I expect I could be held responsible for BRW1's disillusionment with human nature that morning, as I patted him on the head, enjoined him to nick off, and ate the last piece of chocolate myself.

To return to Endora's exploits, having made it past BRW1, she began to wander around the roof near Split. Being a healthy male flying-fox, he soon became interested and began sniffing at her, prompting a flurry of thumb-sparring and sharp vocal exchanges. Endora moved off smartly, energetically pursued by Split. Almost immediately Scruff awoke and joined the fray, beating Split off and taking over his pursuit of the female, sniffing as he went.

There was a brief hiatus when Endora, moving faster and more easily than old Scruff, made her way into the far quadrant, leaving Scruff at the centre ridge (whether his stopping at that point was a question of territorial boundary is debatable). The thwarted Scruff settled close to 010 and Roger, with no sign of objection or rebuff from them, although he was hanging in contact with them. (This was more easily understood in the light of the social arrangements to come, during mating season.)

A few minutes later, Endora was on the move again, this time across the triangles — with the tatty but lively Scruff hot on her heels. That is until he reached halfway across Triangle 2, when he inexplicably abandoned the chase. Endora continued on her way and as BRW1 finally climbed back up from the sapling, she descended once more to its lower branches. This time there were no visitors to offer attention or edible incentives — not even I could stay around. Two hours is a long time on a low log and I badly wanted to creak my way home to restore my circulation to order.

Precisely what Scruff's intentions towards Endora were became, over the ensuing weeks, if anything, less clear. As for Endora's intentions, your guess is as good as mine. My first impression was that this must be the first sign of preliminaries to the formal mating season — procreation rather than random gratuitous sex. In the wild, the summer camps would have been occupied first either by pregnant females or females with young born in scattered maternity camps (Parry-Jones and Augee), after which males and sub-adults born last season would drift in. By December and January the population has usually reached its peak. The breeding females are less taken up with their offspring, the more precocious of whom may even be starting to wean, and the males, free of such encumbrances, begin scouting for mates. They gradually establish tolerance between themselves and their chosen females — the more intimate details will be entered into later. (Nelson, 1965a.)

Not all bats adhere to the pattern of mate selection being a male preserve. In western Africa, the bizarre rainforest megachiropterans known as hammer-headed bats (*Hypsignathus monstrosus*) seem to be one of the very few mammal species to form leks (the others using comparable strategies are some African antelopes). A lek is a group of males which gathers to perform, so to speak, with the aim of impressing females with their genetic potential by calling and flaunting their physiques. It is more often, but not commonly, seen in birds, such as some birds of paradise and species of grouse.

The male *Hypsignathus* is specially equipped for its formidable vocal displays. It has a huge bony larynx occupying approximately one-third of the body cavity, from the throat down into the upper chest, and an inflatable pharyngeal sac. The muzzle is disproportionately large and shaped as the name suggests, with deep folds and ridges of skin. The display is a combination of honking and rapid beating with half-open wings. Females fly around the arena, sometimes hovering in front of a male, at which he increases his calling rate. Should he be the chosen one, he ceases calling while copulating for 30 to 60 seconds, then resumes when the female departs.

To return to *Pteropus*, the mating arrangements might be either a family group — one female with her previous year's young, such as BRW2 formed with 010B — or an adult group. The latter could be a monogamous situation or a harem, such as Scruff was to form with 010, Spot and a characteristically uncooperative Fang. Endora's role in this was ambiguous. The formation of harems has also been recorded in some other species of *Pteropus* such as *P. seychellensis comorensis* (Cheke and Dahl, 1981), *P. rodricensis* (Carroll and Mace, 1988), and *P. m. mariannus* (Wiles, 1987a). (Pierson and Rainey, 1992.)

By February, with mating arrangements sorted out, the selection of territory could begin. This involves a temporary increase in aggression between males until territories (marked with scent from the males' scapular glands) are firmly established. Once this is accomplished, the area will be defended by the females as well as males, although most fights are settled by the males. At this stage, incidentally, most of those youngsters already weaned tend to move away into another area of the camp known as the juvenile pack. This sub-group is supervised by a few unmated adults, mostly males, and is where the young begin learning the conventions of flying-fox society, the rituals of aggression and so on. More adults — predominantly males, with a few associated females — form guard groups around the outer edges of the camp. Not having to cope with the obvious distractions of copulating and defending territories, they act as an early warning system when danger approaches. (Nelson, 1965a.)

Not all species of *Pteropus* form colonies in this way. Some are found only in small groups, others live in pairs or as individuals. There is considerable variation in lifestyles, even among species found within a relatively small area, for instance, the insular flying-fox, *P. tonganus,* and the Samoan flying-fox, *P. samoensis*, in Samoa; the first is what is termed a colonial rooster, that is, one which lives in large groups or camps of several hundred individuals (its local name is *pe'a fai taulaga pe'a* — flying-fox which make flying-fox towns). (Cox, 1983.) *P. samoensis*, however, is often seen alone or in pairs.

Unlike *P. tonganus* and most other pteropids, *P. samoensis* can be observed soaring diurnally, riding the thermals on wings that span nearly 2 metres. In this context it is interesting to note the absence of birds of prey on Samoa, which might otherwise threaten even such a large bat flaunting itself by day. Unfortunately the role of predator is taken on by humans, pigeon hunters and others equipped with firearms. *P. samoensis* differs from *P. tonganus* in another way, a way which also renders it more vulnerable. *P. tonganus* uses secondary forest, whereas *P. samoensis* is restricted to areas of undisturbed (primary) rainforest, a rapidly shrinking habitat. In view of its territorial requirement of about 4 square kilometres, the future for this species would appear uncertain, to say the least. (Cox, op. cit.)

In discussing the habits of flying-foxes, the evidence suggests that we should also take into account the external factors of pressure from human activity, such as hunting and land clearing. *P. samoensis* was described in the 1840s as being present in vast numbers, but due to influences such as the above the population has since declined dramatically.

P. melanotus occurs on a number of islands in the Indian Ocean, including Christmas Island (Australian territory). The population found on Christmas Island shows certain behavioural traits well-suited to the island in its pristine state, however, they have become maladaptive since the alteration of their circumstances brought about by the arrival of Homo sapiens. On an island where it has no natural predators, *P. melanotus* has become diurnal rather than nocturnal (as it remains elsewhere) in its activities, and, like the animals of the Galapagos Islands, fails to recognise even that versatile predator, man, as a threat. Christmas Island remained uninhabited until 1897, but the development of phosphate mining has changed this. It has also changed the nature of the landscape and disturbed areas have become overgrown with thickets of *Muntingia calabura*, a species of shrub or low-growing tree from Central America. Although this fruit-bearing vegetation provides a popular food source for the flying-foxes, it is also frequently their undoing, bringing the feeding animals within easy reach of hunters. The flying-foxes are simply pulled down with steel hooks attached to bamboo poles, then killed with clubs. (Tidemann, 1987.)

On Guam, *P. mariannus*, which is distributed throughout the Mariana Islands of Micronesia, has rather different living arrangements to those of the Australian flying-foxes. Gary Wiles describes camps of between 60 and 800 individuals showing little or no variation in the basic social structure of males with harems of between two and 15 females, one or two bachelor groups (in which some females may be included) of ten to 120, and a small number of solitary males in the outer area of the camp. (A small percentage of the flying-foxes live either singly or in groups of only two to 12 through the day.) Breeding in this species on Guam occurs throughout the year rather than seasonally. (Wiles, G. J. 1987.) Presumably this is a major factor in the consistency of their social organisation through the year and might itself be influenced by food availability, amongst other things. The problems facing the survival of *P. mariannus* on this island will be explained a little later. For some time now, the other species found on Guam (and nowhere else), *P. tokudae*, has been missing, presumed extinct.

As we can see from the grey-headed flying-foxes, pteropid populations can change their roosting patterns quite markedly as seasons bring changes in food availability and the drive to procreate.

John R. and Zita Baker, working in Vanuatu during the 1930s as part of an investigation, 'The Seasons in a Tropical Rainforest: New Hebrides', documented the changes in the population of *P. tonganus geddiei*. This species congregates in large colonies of both sexes on the coast from September through to January, after which the pregnant females disperse until the maternity camps are formed further inland during June. Throughout this period the males remain in the camps near the shore, only dispersing between June and the re-formation of the large coastal camps in September.

Considering the dearth of information about the majority of *Pteropus* species in the wild and the changes in patterns according to season amongst those we are familiar with, it is possible that some now considered solitary, or nearly so, have not always conformed to this lifestyle. *P. giganteus ariel*, which has been observed as a colonial rooster elsewhere, was described by Phillips in 1958 and 1959 as being found as solitary individuals on Addu Atoll. Other species of solitary (or nearly so) habit include *P. pumilus* in the Philippines, *P. griseus griseus* on Timor, *P. livingstonei* in the Comoro Islands, *P. rayneri grandis* on Bougainville, *P. samoensis nawaiensis* of Samoa and *P. temmincki capistratus* of the Bismarck Archipelago. (Pierson and Rainey, 1992.) A habit of roosting alone or in small, scattered groups could be the reason that it has proved so difficult to establish just what the Torresian flying-fox gets up to and where it gets up to it during the hours of daylight.

It is also possible that some species considered rare are less likely to be observed because of their habits. It could be that our view of the roosting habit or population size of a seldom-seen species is to some extent a matter of being in the right place at the right time. Perhaps this could go some of the way towards explaining the mystery of the dusky flying-fox (*P. brunneus*) — that frustrating little bundle of brittle dry skin and fur, lying with its skull in the type specimens cabinet of the Natural History Museum in London. If Captain Denham of HMS *Herald* did in fact find it on one of the Percy Isles, off the Queensland coast, why has no other like it been found? If it was there, is it extinct and if so, why? Perhaps it still exists as a small population living scattered as pairs or individuals. We shall look into this source of brow-beetling and tooth-grinding anon (see chapter 13).

Grey-headed flying-fox (*Pteropus poliocephalus*).

For the time being, there was enough to keep me well and truly bothered amongst the Healesville flying-foxes. On the second day of February came the next revelation in the Scruff and Endora relationship. It was only brief, but nonetheless interesting. I walked into the enclosure just after ten-thirty that morning to find Scruff and Endora hanging together in Triangle 1. He was gently but persistently biting at her, to which she responded by flicking her folded wing at him and uttering a soft 'chuckling' vocalisation, apparently settling the matter.

There was peace until ten past eleven, when Scruff began poking at Endora, hanging less than 15 centimetres from him, in Triangle 2. Rather than retaliating, as I would have expected, she quietly moved away, but only a little further down the triangle. The chuckle vocalisation intrigued me — it was one I had seldom heard, and then only in circumstances when a gentle rebuff was involved, between adult animals otherwise tolerant of each other's proximity.

Four days later (I had been with the bats only briefly in the interim), Scruff was restless in the heat of midday. He moved around the roof from the stinging glare of the apex in full sun, to the deep shade of the smaller triangle within Triangle 1 and, eventually, back again. He briefly sparred and exchanged sharp squawks with the large male BRW1 in Triangle 1. Neither gave ground and they settled not far from each other. There they stayed in the filtered sunlight for the next quarter of an hour before Scruff was on the move again, first circling BRW1, bumping him lightly, without reaction, before pushing past Spot in the full sun of the apex and approaching Endora in Triangle 4. He edged up against her, eliciting no more than a brief chuckle from her, then settled, their bodies bumping gently as they slept. My notes for the following day show that they were again roosting quietly in contact with each other.

So far I had not observed any overtly sexual overtures in the association. However, on 10 February, I arrived to find Scruff and Endora roosting near one another in Triangle 1. For a while they hung wing-wrapped, as still as the cool air of the grey afternoon, then Scruff awoke. Bright, dark eyes glinted in the shadowy depths of his furled wings, then the grizzled, age-thickened muzzle appeared as he looked around to Endora, sniffing at her. They chuckled at each other as she awoke to his examination. A few minutes later Scruff's olfactory inspection moved from Endora's head to her genital area. She chuckled again, this time with slightly more intensity, and hooked gently at his head. At the same time she moved around, but not actually away from him. It was apparently a rebuff, but certainly not of the sort I later saw dealt out by other unwilling females approached in this manner by males. The sun emerged with slow strength, warming the bats and my cold, cramped joints.

The ensuing action drew out over the next five minutes, as in the face of Scruff's insistence, Endora slowly moved away. He followed. Finally, Endora halted in her slow retreat from him. She turned, and still without the usual signs of aggression, began to force him backwards. When Scruff had retreated to her satisfaction, the two flying-foxes stopped, about 30 centimetres apart, and rested. As the sun resumed the cover of the clouds, Scruff and Endora drew their wings around themselves, effectively drawing the curtains on the interlude.

While this quiet and unhurried action was in progress, on the other side of the quadrants a more typical piece of pteropid drama was in progress, accompanied by the customary sharp utterances and vigorous application of thumb hooks. Split, in the course of his wanderings, had met the youngster 001B and begun sniffing, to be set upon by the nearby female Fang. (She had shortly before sent him packing with a vocal rebuff when he had crossed her path.) In the face of this disturbance the rather retiring male Pale began to withdraw quietly from the scene, only to be hooked and squawked at by the larger BRW2, causing him to retreat more hastily from the apex.

A couple of days later I was interested to see Endora approaching Scruff. As my session began they had been sleeping 30 centimetres or so apart in Triangle 1. There they remained until 20 minutes later, when Endora awoke and clambered down into the usual sapling to inspect the offerings of some schoolboys. Before long she returned by the same route to the roof, then, to my surprise, flew to the area above my head. It was most unusual for one of this group to fly rather than walk under these circumstances. Perhaps it was a matter of greater than usual urgency. As I followed the direction of her gaze, I saw that the boys had left the

Kingfisher

remains of their banana on the log opposite my perch. Obviously, discretion was the better part of greed — after five minutes of concentrated banana-watching, Endora turned and began walking back toward the apex. (As this species of flying-fox seems reluctant to descend to the ground and is thoroughly uneasy if it does, I was fascinated to watch the Rodrigues flying-foxes, *Pteropus rodricensis,* at the Jersey Wildlife Preservation Trust fluttering to the ground to pick up food, moving around in a relaxed manner before flying back up to their roost.) Endora kept moving until she had reached her former roost, close to Scruff. I waited to record his reaction (if any) to her approach. At this juncture one of the other inhabitants of the enclosure, a tiny jewel-like sacred kingfisher, contrived to get its head stuck in the wire mesh of the roof and hung there struggling in panic. I left quickly to alert a keeper. As it happened, the little wretch managed to extricate itself just as help arrived.

The next day brought further gentle pursuit of Endora by Scruff and the familiar mild rebuffs of chuckling and shaking of a closed wing (rather than actual hooking) as he sniffed at her genital area. There was also some 'mouthing', without biting, combined with the exchange of chuckling vocalisations. Scruff desisted and they settled about 45 centimetres apart. Despite the genital sniffing, Scruff was not making any serious attempts at mating as far as I was able to observe. I was puzzled, as, where such things are concerned, subtlety is not the male flying-fox's forte as a rule. However, this was how it continued with Scruff and Endora, as February gave way to March. Looking back through the roosting maps, there were few observation sessions when they were not hanging more or less together, usually in Triangle 1.

The observation notes for 13 March remark that this was the first time since their association began that Scruff and Endora had been seen so far apart. She was inspecting visitors in her sapling while he roosted in Quadrant 1. This seems to mark the beginning of a change in the relationship, even though the patterns of pursuit, quiet chuckle vocalisations, mouthing and mild rebuffs continued. Two days later, for the first time, I saw Scruff actually nuzzling at Endora's genital area, rather than simply sniffing. This was the usual preliminary to a serious attempt at copulation. In this case, however, the attempt was not serious enough for Scruff to persist after the accustomed low-key rebuff and Endora removing herself to a distance of 22 or so centimetres. During the ensuing five minutes, each turned its attention to grooming, Scruff stopping momentarily to crane his neck and sniff at Endora's head and shoulders, to which she showed no reaction. A moment later each was cloaked in leathery wings and incommunicado.

On 18 March, I entered the enclosure to a chorus of loud braying. I scanned the roof and saw that the racket was being produced by Scruff as he wrangled with 010. They broke apart, 010 maintaining her position while Scruff moved around her in a 30-centimetre radius, the two still in an apparently aggressive mood. Actually, it was fairly typical of the end of a pteropid sexual encounter — at least for this species. What seemed slightly unusual was that Scruff took advantage of a couple of lulls in the action to exchange mild chuckle vocalisations with Endora. The next day he was following her as usual.

Thus things continued between Scruff and Endora (I did not see him repeating his efforts with 010 in the interim) until 2 April. I noticed that day that Endora's vulva was convulsing with rapid and consistent spasms. How long it had been doing so before I noticed, I have no idea, but over the next five minutes they continued, before becoming less regular and a few minutes later she turned away, making further observation impossible. I wondered whether Scruff — or one of the others for that matter — had finally mated with her. Next day most of the bats, including Endora and Scruff, remained irritatingly inactive, swathed in their dark cloaks of wing. However, on the following day it appeared that Scruff had taken to consorting with 010. He made two approaches to Endora, sniffing at her, only to be rebuffed first with a chattering vocalisation, then a second time, more aggressively, before she moved away. There was no sign of the mild chuckling of the weeks gone by. Scruff did not follow her the second time, but moved instead to his earlier roost, hooking at the nearby male SM, before settling. The special relationship between Scruff and Endora was over.

CHAPTER 9

Scruff

A number of things were going on while I was busy trying to unravel the complexities of Scruff's relationship with Endora. Out in the wild camps, from about January onward, the breeding males were concluding the business of mate(s) selection and establishing their territories. Having formed either family groups, with a female and last year's young, or adult groups, with one or more females but no young, the males were becoming more aggressive. February usually sees the peak of the territorial fighting, which lessens as neighbours fix and learn their boundaries. John Nelson found males with harems to be more aggressive and territorial than the monogamous ones. Once territories are established the flying-foxes are able to concentrate their energies on mating.

In the Healesville group, I was at last able to identify 010B as a female and christen her Lucy. There was no particular reason for the choice of name other than that it was the first to occur to me. This has subsequently been the case with a number of bats and I often find that these are the easiest names to remember. As the numbers grew in years to come, any aid to memory was welcome.

According to the accepted wisdom on the timing of the grey-headed flying-fox's peak of procreative enthusiasm, the Healesville group seemed a little slow off the mark, assuming, of course, that they were not at it like knives the moment my back was turned throughout the early autumn. The association between Scruff and Endora had not led where I expected, so now, well into April, I waited to see what would develop between the old fellow and 010.

At this stage Roger was becoming more independent, but still returning from time to time to suckle, although it may have been more a question of comfort or habit rather than actually obtaining nourishment from 010. At six months of age he probably would have been well and truly ensconced in a juvenile pack had he been born in the wild. Lucy, slightly younger, was still more dependent on 010B, spending more time at her mother's breast and occasionally demonstrating considerable determination to stay there. I watched one day in early April as 010B attempted to move away from her now rather large offspring, who was hanging beside her but champing quietly at her breast. I suppose it shows a want of sympathy, but I was in grave danger of falling off my log and interrupting my observations, laughing as poor 010 toiled around the roof in a small circle, firmly anchored by Lucy's teeth clamped on her left nipple.

On 22 April, a chilly, still morning barely touched by the sun's warmth as the early mist disappeared, I began to see more clearly the patterns which would dominate the next few weeks' observations. As the patterns emerged, so did a number of questions.

What determined who would mate the females? BRW2 was clearly dominant by the accepted yardsticks: a big, stroppy animal (the heaviest?), able to displace others and chase other males from his partner(s). Scruff 'won' some interactions, but lost others, pestered rather than 'heavied' females, and was reasonably well tolerated. He was large but physically in poor condition, with badly healed wing breaks, and scars liberally scattered around his muzzle and wing membranes. As no serious fighting over females or challenges had been observed, and the mating pattern of BRW2, BRWF and 010B persisted over several years, could it be that Scruff had established dominance when younger and fitter and that he had some sort of ongoing *droit de seigneur* with the females 010, Spot and Endora? Or do social and manipulative skills play some role (as in Shirley Strum's observations on baboons) (Strum, 1987).

In the course of the morning I noticed that Scruff was able to force a retreat by SM when an interaction took place in Triangle 1, but retreated himself when the situation occurred in Triangle 2 (SM's usual haunt). On retreating from the latter encounter, Scruff soon turned his attention to Spot, exchanging a brief rain of hook-blows and squeals with her before returning to his position in Triangle 1. Meanwhile, 010B reluctantly allowed Lucy back onto her breast and began moving back along the high central ridge, where she was intercepted by BRW2.

BRW2 was a rather easier bat to 'read' than Scruff. After a flurry of hooking and chattering vocalisations with 010B, he proceeded to trail her across the roof, pausing to chase Split away when 010B's path crossed his. BRW2 doggedly pestered 010B, despite her vigorous biting and hooking (presumably somewhat hampered by the fact that Lucy was still firmly on board). Throughout a series of tussles BRW2 kept up a penetrating two-note braying sound I came to think of as the 'coital anthem'.

This may be the basis for the idea that rape is a popular pastime with flying-foxes, as it is often difficult to tell which animal is responsible for the racket and it certainly sounds more likely to come from the assailed than the assailant. In this instance the vocal drama continued past the physical interaction, while BRW2 hung separately, scratching and grooming himself. I was interested to note that his penis remained detumescent throughout the encounter. Over the years I have found that the braying vocalisation almost invariably accompanies mounting, whether intromission is carried through or not. It could function as a sort of territorial or claiming call, warning other males off the female thus favoured. I have also heard it used by BRW2 when chasing Split away, after the latter had approached 010B during the period of intensive mating activity.

Similar vocalisations drew my attentions to the other side of the roof, where Scruff had begun pestering 010 and Spot. The whole thing remained somewhat lower key than BRW2 and 010B's performance, perhaps because Scruff's attention was divided. The females' rebuffs were also less vigorous and Scruff continued to harass Spot in a desultory fashion for another five minutes or so, before moving away. And so things continued for the rest of the observation session, another quarter of an hour or so, with Scruff winning an encounter with the youngish male, Pale, trying his luck once more with Spot and a couple of times with Endora, meeting rebuffs from both. He turned from Endora's final rejection to approach 010, accepting a quick, mild rebuff from her too. On the other side of the roof, BRW2's charms had similarly failed to impress 010B again.

Perhaps symbolically, it was Anzac Day, 25 April, when I finally saw the consummation of Scruff and BRW2's efforts. By the end of the day I felt rather like pinning a medal on the latter! It was one of those mornings that seem made for idling outside, watching the breeze chase gentle shafts of light through the gum leaves, and stretching out on the grass, in spite of what your mother told you about lying on damp ground. Just before nine o'clock, the temperature was on its way to 22 degrees Celsius and the bats, less inclined to laziness than I, were all actively grooming, scratching and stretching. Ten minutes into the session, Scruff set the tone for the day, with his first approaches to Spot, who rebuffed him, then to 010, who simply ignored him.

At eight minutes past ten BRW2 began his campaign, hooking at Lucy to drive her further from her mother, on whom he had designs. With 010B's offspring sent packing, BRW2 began vigorously licking and nuzzling the area of her vulva, breaking his intense activity only briefly to lick at his penis. The latter was not such a feat as one might think. The appearance of the male flying-fox's fully erect external genitalia suggests that Heath Robinson might have assisted the Almighty in their design. The penis is roughly half the length of the animal's body, not to mention being capable, to some extent, of 'independent' movement. These astonishing facts, however, cut no ice with 010B that morning. She remained impassive throughout this pteropid foreplay.

Ten minutes after beginning, BRW2 suddenly stopped licking and moved swiftly behind the female. He grasped her auburn ruff in his teeth and mounted her for a frenetic 30 seconds. As he released his grip they scuffled and chattered rapidly before he once more managed to get behind 010B, this time reaching around to lick her as before. Two minutes later BRW mounted again. This time coitus lasted for a full minute, in spite of 010B hauling herself around the roof wire still in his clasp. On being released she turned to hook and bite at him.

Loud braying from the other side of the roof drew my eye to Scruff being beaten off by a similarly biting and flailing 010. Meanwhile BRW2 had resumed his pre-coital grooming of 010B. In the space of 42 minutes, he managed to mount 11 times, at least five of which appeared to result in intromission.

As I prepared to close the observation session, Spot and 010 began moving toward the apex of the triangles — the latter with Scruff, penis erect, hauling himself across the wire in pursuit. This time he was able to do no more than sniff 010 before being quietly rebuffed with a quack, and he settled, after a quick penis lick and groom, 30 centimetres or so from her. Seeing all the animals neatly wrapped up and quiet at last, I juggled my paraphernalia — binoculars, tripod, camera, notes, sketchbook, recording book and tape recorder — into some sort of awkward but portable arrangement and left them to it.

The reproductive anatomy of *Pteropus* is interesting in a number of ways. There are three basic versions of the uterine arrangement in placental (not marsupial or monotreme) mammals. Humans, anthropoid apes and some bat species are among the animals with a simplex uterus, which means that the two horns have fused into one for their entire length and have a single cervical canal leading into the vagina. The second basic design is the bicornuate uterus, which has two horns that are joined externally from the end nearest the cervix for between 5% and 50% of their length. They are also joined internally at the end nearest the single cervical canal. *Pteropus* is equipped with the third 'design option'. The uterus is duplex, that is, each oviduct opens into a separate horn. The left and right uterine horns lead into two cervical canals, which open into the vagina. (Wynn, R. M. and Jollie, W. P. (Eds).) Each of the three uterine forms is represented among the chiropterans.

Although there are two horns to the uterus, and two functioning ovaries, most

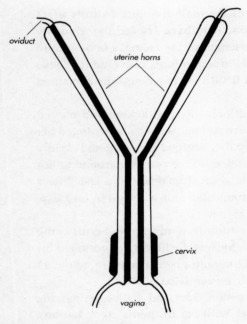

oviduct

uterine horns

cervix

vagina

The duplex uterus of *Pteropus*.

members of *Pteropus* appear to ovulate on only one side each season and produce single young. There are exceptions, and Martin et al. (1987) mention instances where superfoetation has occurred, that is, a second conception has taken place some time after fertilisation of the first egg, resulting in embryos of different ages, rather than what we normally regard as twins.

Its Brobdingnagian proportions are by no means the most interesting feature of the male flying-fox's copulatory implement. Mammal penises achieve and maintain the rigidity they need for efficient intromission and sperm delivery in a number of ways. Some animals have a baculum or os penis, in other words a penis bone; in others the penis is fibroelastic and remains in a perpetual state of semi-erection. In the higher primates and bats the erection depends upon a vascular system within the penis, which allows it to become engorged with blood and thus enlarged and stiffened. Some bat species have a penis bone as well, although this is usually small. The major erectile role-players are the long cylinders of spongy tissue known as corpora cavernosa, which lie along the shaft of the penis. Surrounding the urethra, there is another body of tissue richly supplied with blood vessels, called the corpus spongiosum. This is common to most mammals to some degree or other. However, a corpus spongiosum extending right along the shaft and expanding right into the head of the penis is a feature apparently restricted to an elite group amongst the mammals, namely, megachiropterans, dermopterans (colugos; see chapter 2) and primates. Do we lump it in with the common wiring of brains as convergent evolution or regard these as evolutionary links and regard flight as something which evolved twice, rather than once from a common ancestor of mega- and microchiropterans? The jury will undoubtedly be out for some time yet.

The testes of grey-headed flying-foxes wax and wane in size seasonally, as do those of other *Pteropus* species studied. (Baker and Baker, 1936, *P. geddiei*, and Marshall, 1947, *P. giganteus*.)

BRW2 approaches 010B with a view to mating; BRWF looks on.

Some birds of paradise form leks, where the females select their mates from the group of male performers. This is also seen in the hammer-headed bat (*Hypsignathus monstrosus*).

According to McGuckin and Blackshaw (1984, 1987a) the increase in size begins in October, continuing until February/March, at roughly which time the production of sperm is also at its peak. The abundance of sperm in the epididymus (the tube through which sperm move from the testes to be stored and ripened, then progress through the vas deferens for eventual delivery) peaks in April. Regression then begins and continues until June. These findings came from a study of wild animals. Further investigation under laboratory conditions showed that the testis growth starts in September. (Martin et al., 1987.)

An experiment carried out by McGuckin and Blackshaw (1985) was able to confirm earlier scientists' hypotheses that this male cycle, which includes the fluctuation of testosterone levels and bodyweight, is governed by the relative lengths of daylight and night. In other words, photoperiod. By the time autumn arrives with its shorter days, the males are in prime condition for an all-out effort to impregnate females.

I found it interesting that throughout the study of the Healesville flying-foxes, Pale's genitalia remained markedly smaller than those of other adult males. According to Nelson's estimations based on testis weight, male grey-headed flying-foxes are sexually mature at around 18 months old, and I was able to watch the rates of development of Roger and subsequent generations of male offspring for comparison to Pale, who was 20 months old when I began. There was also SM, who was one year younger. Pale remained not only underdeveloped, but apparently at the bottom of the pecking order. Over the years I saw him make only one rather awkward attempt to mount a female, which he gave up almost as soon as he started. By contrast, Roger was copulating like a professional, with his long-suffering mother, two weeks short of his first birthday.

It is possible for conceptions to occur outside the neat pattern described — at least three births have occurred in the Healesville colony in February, which implies that successful matings occurred in August or September. In two cases this out-of-season mating corresponds to the introduction of a group of three males and three females from the quarantine area, where they had been held since late April, into the enclosure in August 1987. (The other February birth occurred in 1987.) Which brings us back to the females. Here the case is rather less clear than with the males. Why do most females conceive during a relatively short period of time, shorter than that in which high-level mating activity is occurring? Jock Marshall (1947) in his study of the Indian flying-fox, surmised that the female ovulates in response to the stimulation of mating. This would probably mean stimulation of receptors in the cervix and neuronal pathways to the hypothalamus in the brain, in turn causing the pituitary gland beneath it to secrete the hormonal trigger for ovulation (pituitary luteinising hormone).

For female grey-headed flying-foxes, the answer is not so simple. It is possible that day length has some influence over the release of hormones from the pituitary gland triggering ovulation. The studies carried out by Len Martin's team suggest that male activity in terms of glandular odour and vocalisation has some influence. Lactation could also play a role by suppressing ovulation, although in the Healesville group I could not be sure whether 010B's late-suckling offspring were actually obtaining milk from her. In some mammals the continuing stimulus of regular suckling can prolong lactation. 010B habitually allowed her offspring to suckle well past the onset of serious mating activity and did not conceive (judging by the birthdates of the subsequent offspring) until copulations had been occurring for some weeks. I often saw BRW2 either trying to copulate with 010B while a well-grown youngster was attached to her breast, or driving her offspring away in order to do so. On one occasion I observed Lucy, clinging to her mother's breast, occasionally releasing the nipple to lean across and lick BRW2's neck while he assiduously groomed 010B's vulva.

The experience of the University of Queensland team indicates that lactation does not delay or prevent conception. Their experimental work and observation of how births are distributed shows that although the females do not ovulate before a certain date, they are capable of doing so repeatedly beyond that. This may mean that the secretion of gonadotrophin is affected by relative daylength, possibly through the reaction of the pineal gland to increasing and decreasing periods of light.

The work of Len Martin and company, although not entirely eliminating the possibility of reflex ovulation occurring under some circumstances in grey-headed flying-foxes (see out-of-season births on page 99) shows that this species can ovulate spontaneously. This being so, certain questions arise about the restriction of uterine growth to one horn of the bicornuate uterus. In other mammals ovulating spontaneously, a surge of oestrogen from the developing ovarian follicle stimulates a surge of luteinising hormone from the pituitary gland. This is responsible for ovulation, through positive feedback on the hypothalamus. However, in the grey-headed flying-fox the fact that only one horn of the uterus develops implies that the ovarian oestrogens do not flood the animal's general circulation. The question remains as to how an ovary can communicate with the hypothalamus, and with the neighbouring uterine horn, whilst excluding the one opposite. Martin et al. suggest the possibility of a novel ovarian steroid as a messenger. (L. Martin, pers. comm., 1994.)

By late April it was clear that Scruff was bent on distributing his favours more widely than BRW2, who favoured the 'all the eggs in one basket' approach, and made very sure the eggs were fertilised. Scruff spread himself — and his genes —

more thinly and was less thorough. Whether it was a matter of age and infirmity or simply a difference between individuals is difficult to say, but Scruff's approach to copulation was less businesslike than that of BRW2. Scruff's bristly, grizzled old face, with its thick snout and battered looking ears, gave an impression of world-weariness. The scarred and knobbly wings were not much use for flying and as I watched him hauling himself around the roof after sundry females, I often wondered where he would find the stamina to copulate if he caught one. Unlike BRW2 with 010B, Scruff wasted little time on the unwilling.

The events of 29 April were not an unusual example. Scruff began by nuzzling Endora, who showed no sign of cooperating. Eighteen minutes later he was licking the genitals of Spot, who fairly smartly rebuffed the advance. Barely pausing for breath the old fellow launched into similar foreplay with the nearby 010, with an unsatisfactory result. His next move was to return to and mount Spot, braying lustily throughout a 20-second intromission, and beyond. The racket stopped two minutes later as he once again began grooming Spot's genital area. By the time I looked back to him, four minutes later, Scruff was engaged in an attempt to get behind 010 in order to mount her. He kept this up for the next minute before abandoning the effort.

This far into the mating season I found that I was sufficiently well acquainted with the general procedures for interesting subtleties to become apparent. I had become adept at recording times and basic vocal responses through BRW2's breakneck sessions, without being fazed, even by regularly having to explain to visitors that the animals were not engaged in a fight to the death and certainly needed no assistance from a keeper in their struggles. Sometimes it was easy to understand the anxieties of the uninitiated, watching BRW2's rugby tackle approach to procreation — particularly on the day that 010B ended a bout flapping frantically in midair, dangling by a tuft of her scalp hair from BRW2's teeth.

Scruff's pre-copulatory grooming was a more refined affair, which sometimes included non-genital grooming. For instance, on 1 May I found him hanging in the cool, drizzly morning air, grooming Spot's vulva, an overture quickly rebuffed. He moved immediately to 010, nudging her, only to receive a quiet vocal rebuff. Without protest he simply redirected his attention to Endora and began rubbing the back of his head on her wings (possibly trying to transfer scent from his scapular glands). At this Endora 'quack-chuckled' at him, using the vocalisation I had not heard since the period of her earlier association with Scruff. It seemed to indicate tolerance, as she pulled back her folded wings, allowing the old bat to nuzzle her right 'armpit'. (I noticed that with other females too, his repertoire included similar nuzzling, as well as licking of the wing membranes and body.) This continued for a couple of minutes until a quiet vocal rebuff from Endora brought it to an undramatic conclusion. Scruff went off to 010, sniffed at her, then settled nearby, encased in his stiff knobbly wings. This peaceful interlude was accompanied by the racket of BRW2 and 010B going hammer and tongs with similar intent on the other side of the cage. However, despite their more frenetic style, 010B gave me my first opportunity to identify the female 'clockwork churring' vocalisation during intromission.

The following day brought further revelations from BRW2 and 010B. The nature of their couplings changed in style and duration. The entry in my notebook reads: '. . . 2-minute, 4-second coition. Different to previously observed. No vocalisations after mounting until very quiet muttering by 010B shortly preceding release. No rapid thrusting — only occasional convulsive thrusts. During last minute 010B's feet in space, loose grip on wire with one thumb, but principally supported by BRW2. 010B's eyes appear to bulge.'

Looking back on these notes and others at the time and doing some rough calculations back from the dates of birth of the two youngsters born in the following November, I began to wonder whether there was some connection between the change in style and conception. Whether the 'little but often' pattern, — many short rather frantic copulations for an hour or so at a time throughout the day — could be involved in triggering ovulation and that the longer intromissions of the style described above take place when the female is ready to conceive. The day after I first noticed the change in copulatory style, it appeared that although the intromissions were longer, they were still frequent — 13 in the space of one hour, at the end of which a whitish fluid could be seen dribbling from 010B's vulva. BRW2 licked very briefly at it then retired to rest.

At this time there seemed to be a hiccup in Scruff's reproductive efforts. I noticed what looked like a small pink lesion below the head of his penis, but could not be sure whether there was actually something amiss with him, or whether it was simply the small patch of papillae, somewhat like the texture of a cat's tongue. Presumably this patch assists in keeping the penis in position during intromission. Judging by a number of aborted mountings and his extra grooming of the area, Scruff seemed bothered by it. However, within a few days the pinkness was less noticeable and Scruff was, like BRW2, changing to the more extended style of intromission. He also began making the odd advance to Spot's daughter Fang in his rounds.

010, who, during the observation sessions at least, appeared the most obliging of his harem, provided some excellent opportunities to record the female accompaniment to the 'coital anthem' in full. It began with a quiet, almost mechanical churring, rising in volume and intensity until the male released her, when there would be a flurry of vocalisations, biting or mouthing and hooking with outstretched thumbs. They would also continue braying. Typically, the animals would then draw apart to groom themselves.

When I began a shortened session with the flying-foxes in the late afternoon of 16 May, I expected little action. It was a still, grey day and the air had a chill to it. Scruff, however, undaunted, was pursuing Endora around the roof as I walked in, seizing each opportunity as she slowed down or stopped to lick at her genital area. Her response was to chuckle at him and move away. The old fellow eventually gave up and joined some of the others at the feeding station, rather than, as on the preceding day and so many others, transferring his attentions to other favoured females in turn until one proved cooperative.

Illness kept me away from the flying-foxes for the next few days and when I returned there was obviously something wrong. SM was pursuing 010, something I had not seen before. Attempts at mating had been restricted to BRW2 and Scruff; the latter was nowhere to be seen. Although I felt uneasy, it was not unusual to lose sight of an animal. They occasionally came down into the fronds of a palm, or were difficult to locate in the dark area behind the feeding shelter. I decided that the old chap must simply be out of sight and settled back to enjoy the spectacle of one of the others, hanging by its thumbs to urinate and scoring a direct hit on the head of a female visitor.

The next day Scruff was still not in evidence and I combed the bushes and ground area for him. Knowing that his ancient wings were not much use, I thought he might have come a cropper amongst the ferns or long grass. There was no sign of him. Some time later a keeper arrived and I learned that my guess was right, but it had happened some hours after I had last seen him — Scruff had been dead for almost a week. SM had already started taking over his females.

Some time during the night or early morning after I had last seen Scruff at the feeding station he had apparently come to grief by falling from the roof. When the keeper arrived to clean the enclosure, he found the old fellow on the ground — his toes were hooked into the wire of the wall, but he seemed paralysed. Soon after, the vet confirmed that his back was broken and Scruff was euthanased. The post mortem revealed that he had kidney stones, the kidneys were pale red and blotched and there was evidence of cortical adenoma and enlarged adrenals. He was probably about 19 years old, a good age for a flying-fox.

It was some time before I stopped automatically casting my eye over the left quadrants in search of Scruff during observation sessions. Objectively, he had become one of the cornerstones of the study, but I realised that he was more to me than that. There was little of detached scientific attitude in my reaction to his death. Subsequently other bats left the group or, in one case, disappeared, but it was never the same as the loss of grubby, snorting and sneezing, ramshackle Scruff.

CHAPTER 10

The Birth of Richard

There was always something different about BRWF. She was smallish and darker than the others, with a handsome deep chestnut ruff. BRWF arrived at Taronga Zoo, from Annandale, Sydney, on 25 February, 1984, and was registered as an adult weighing 600 grams. Three years and two months later she was transferred to Healesville Sanctuary, along with 010B, BRW2, Scruff, Endora, and the male LBW. I could find nothing in the records to indicate that she had bred at either institution.

Of all the animals in the Healesville group, BRWF was the least sociable and, as far as I could see, the least mobile. Although she had little contact with any of the others, her territory of about 1 to 1.5 square metres was right beside the habitual roost of BRW2, the big male. Even when the others scattered, alarmed by some sound or sight, BRWF rarely moved more than half a metre out of her small domain.

My interest in her behaviour intensified during the 1989 mating season described in the previous chapter. On 5 May, as I hurriedly scribbled a note on BRW2's genital grooming of 010B, I was astonished to see BRWF approach the pair, hooking and sniffing at BRW2. He responded peremptorily with a vocal rebuff, at the same time lashing out with a thumb claw, before resuming his pre-copulatory ritual with 010B. There is a description in John Nelson's behavioural study of female flying-foxes soliciting the sexual attentions of males and I presume that this was the case with BRWF. However, in view of her usual habits, I was surprised at her initiating any sort of contact.

What there might have been in the way of interactions between BRWF and BRW2 in the interim, I have no way of knowing. However, a few days later, 010B moved away from BRW2 and his persistent vigorous foreplay. This time, rather than following her, he simply transferred the activity to an apparently obliging BRWF. The attention was shortlived. One minute later, 010B returned to BRW2's territory and he commenced grooming her as before, deserting BRWF without ceremony.

On the last day of May, after weeks of intensive mating activity, 010B rebuffed BRW2's sexual advances with, it appeared, greater conviction than usual. Sufficient at least for him to give up forthwith and move over to where BRWF was roosting. He sniffed at her, then began licking and nuzzling her genital area. She responded vocally, but with no more physical sign of a rebuff. The two began moving slowly around the roof — for once BRWF was venturing well outside her territory and, for that matter, well outside the usual area frequented by BRW2. Although moving around, BRWF was evidently being more cooperative during pre-copulatory activity than the other females I had observed. It is impossible to know just how much actual copulation went on between BRWF and BRW2. My records show some fairly desultory efforts at mating on 15 and 16 August of that year. Nevertheless, at some point conception was achieved.

As winter deepened, the hours of cold observation were occasionally relieved by a burst of song from the nearby lyrebird enclosure or the scuffling and musical yelping of the dingoes next door, sorting out some domestic issue of their own. The was little activity amongst the flying-foxes. I sat doggedly, growing numb in mind and hindquarters, waiting for the brief unwrapping of wings which might reveal signs of pregnancy in the females. I was briefly seized by the notion that it would be interesting to test urine samples from them and for a couple of weeks, lurked below, receptacle at the ready, for a female to upend herself. The animals seemed to regard this with suspicion and invariably changed their minds at the sight of me with plastic container poised to collect. I changed my tactics to spreading my transparent plastic rain cloak on the ground and hovering with a syringe ready to draw up the puddles of piddle I expected. They restrained themselves or did it elsewhere. I decided it was pointless anyway and resumed wearing the rain cloak instead. A few days later, as I crouched in this confection of pink see-through plastic, folding stool and legs concealed beneath a skirt, a very small boy stared long and hard before tugging at his teacher's sleeve and whispering, 'Is that the fairy tooth lady?'.

By October I was pleased, although rather surprised, to see BRWF growing interestingly plump. As was 010B, which did not surprise me at all. On the other side of the cage, 010, Endora, Spot and Fang remained their sylph-like selves. Scruff's last stand had apparently been in vain.

It became easier to monitor the progress of the pregnancies as the sun broke through more frequently, inducing the two females to draw back their wings and bask, warming their widening bellies. As far as I could make out, BRWF must have been at least six or seven years old, rather late for a first birth for a grey-headed flying-fox.

Shortly after midday on 28 October, the breeze dropped, the sky cleared and the chill left the air. The bats began stretching and folding back their wings to bask in the gentle sunlight. As BRWF exposed the rich sepia fur of her now distended belly, I noticed a flash of pinkish-red in the darkness. Adjusting my binoculars I could just discern a small, glistening protuberance at her vulva. She had begun to prolapse. It was at that stage minor, but did not seem to augur well. I wondered how much longer she could carry the foetus.

For the next seven days I watched. The prolapse was most obvious when BRWF was grooming, but it was not until 3 November that it showed any sign of worsening, appearing as three rather than two small fleshy lobes. Even so, it did not seem to bother the bat unduly; she behaved normally and did not even pay particular attention to that area when grooming. A day later, there was a noticeable change in BRWF's shape — the lateral spread of her belly had been transformed into a forward bulge in the lower abdomen. The foetus was apparently moving into position for delivery.

The next day, 5 November, was Sunday and the temptation to play truant and stay in bed with a pot of coffee and the weekend papers was stronger than usual. Eventually, the thought of BRWF and her promising bulge prevailed. At ten to ten I entered the enclosure and immediately noticed that the pink prolapse had been replaced by a small dark elbow and wing-tip emerging from BRWF's vagina. A keeper told me that she had been grooming intensively when he came to service the area at nine o'clock. Now she hung, mostly wing-wrapped, but intermittently grooming; only twice, however, licking the genital area. This continued for the next hour, with no obvious sign of distress and no evidence of contractions. Elbow first is no way for a flying-fox to enter the world and not much progress could be made without veterinary intervention. Not knowing how long the foetus had been in this position, it was difficult to be overly optimistic about the prospect of a live birth.

At eleven o'clock all was at last ready. Dr Rosie Booth, now the sanctuary's vet, had raced to the sanctuary to set up the operating facility, keeping staff arrived with a long-handled net and BRWF was quickly and quietly caught. Extracted from the net struggling, she was swiftly transferred to a cloth bag and spirited across the sanctuary to the treatment centre.

If I was initially delighted, having met her in Brisbane, to see Rosie appointed as the sanctuary's vet, I was doubly pleased to see her there that morning. Not just a competent veterinarian, but one experienced in the treatment of flying-foxes!

BRWF was removed from the bag and anaesthetised, allowing Rosie to assess the situation. A small group of keepers and I watched tensely as she manipulated the foetus, pushing gently on the elbow and wing-tip and eventually managing to turn the baby in the birth canal before drawing it from the vagina in a normal head-first position.

Rosie, cradling the lifeless-looking bundle of glistening skin and shrivelled membrane in one hand, carefully inserted an endotracheal tube into its minute black maw to suck away any blockage of mucus. The tiny animal's airway was cleared, and as Rosie opened her hand we watched it draw breath for the first time.

Loosely swaddled in a towel and already writhing uncertainly, the youngster was handed to a keeper, who cradled it to her. Instinctively searching for a nipple, it fastened its jaws around her conveniently located shirt button and began to suck. Its prospects seemed to be improving by the minute. Now our main concern was for the mother.

Our elation at the delivery of a live, if somewhat 'undercooked' infant cooled rapidly at the sight of BRWF's uterus prolapsing in the wake of the afterbirth. I watched in admiration as Rosie calmly stuffed the lot back where it came from, neatly purse stitching the vagina, to prevent re-expulsion, leaving the umbilicus outside and enough slack in the stitching to permit the exit of the placenta in the prescribed manner. Oxytocin was administered to expedite the separation of the placenta from the uterus, and while the two animals rested, we all discussed the next problem.

The placenta would need a little help in getting through the stitched area and the obvious solution seemed to be to attach a very small weight to the umbilical cord; gravity would provide the necessary encouragement. Simplicity itself...until we applied ourselves to the matter of precisely what could be used as a weight. Tension mounted as we racked our brains and an edge of mild hysteria developed as the suggestions became wilder with each rejection on one ground or another. Finally, someone stumbled on the obvious — a metal nut. They are available in a suitable range of sizes, with a convenient hole through the middle for easy attachment — it was perfect. However, other than those actually holding together vital pieces of equipment or parts of the structure, there was nary a one to be found in the surgery. By the time one of the keepers contacted maintenance staff on the two-way radio, only to be asked did we want cashews or peanuts, the whites of our eyes were showing and the response to the laughter crackling through the handset was a burst of unparliamentary language.

A selection of nuts arrived and one of a suitable weight was chosen. This was attached to a thread and held by a couple of stitches to the end of the umbilicus. As the mother recovered, it was time to introduce her to the cause of all her troubles. The youngster, by now rather more recognisable as an infant *Pteropus*, was laid on BRWF's front and without hesitation seized the nearest nipple. It would be difficult to describe the scene as attractive but, in view of the morning's events, it seemed to me a perfectly wonderful sight.

Mother and young spent the next few hours in a warm recovery box before being transferred to a holding cage in the treatment centre. I was almost surprised, under the circumstances, to hear that in spite of her trauma, BRWF's maternal instinct was functioning well. When the infant lost its grip during the transfer and became disoriented, searching for a teat around the vulva and the weight attached to the umbilicus, she gently grasped its head in her mouth and placed it on the nipple, where it resumed suckling. By the following morning the placenta had been successfully expelled.

The new member of the study group became known as Richard. I named him after a friend whose attitude to flying-foxes needed improving. My greatest concern now was establishing whether the infant had in fact been carried to full term and, if not, to estimate the degree of prematurity. The best sources I could think of were Helen Luckhoff, Len Martin and Lorraine Little. Among them they had seen more newborn flying-foxes than most people have had hot dinners and Lorraine very kindly compiled a list of characteristics and their variables in full-term and premature births. From this I surmised that Richard was perhaps a week or so premature. His eyes at birth were still slits, just showing signs of opening. His back was thinly covered with fine, very short hair. There was some slightly longer fur on the crown of his head and the nape of his neck, where it was dark ginger, but the facial area was all but bald, with vertical wrinkles along the sides. Nevertheless, judging by the grip he had on the maternal food source, if he didn't survive it would not be for lack of trying.

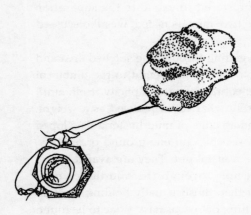

The placenta — slightly chewed by BRWF — with nut attached, after a difficult birth.

Nine days after giving birth, BRWF was fit enough to be reintroduced to the flying-fox enclosure. I decided to spend the whole day with the group to see whether she would encounter any problems and to chart the activity levels of the animals over a number of hours. In the intervening period (on 11 November), 010B had given birth to a daughter. There had been other changes in recent months. Endora and BRW1 had been removed — Endora to join another female, Witch, in an off-exhibit area and BRW1 to a private zoo in South Australia. LBW had simply disappeared without trace. His thumb band with his identity number was found months later just outside the sanctuary.

Early on the morning of 14 November we assembled at the flying-fox enclosure — keepers with the safely bagged bats, I, slung about with notebooks, sketchbooks, tape recorder, camera equipment, folding chair and large thermos of coffee, determined to spend my day in some sort of comfort. The bats in the aviary were immediately suspicious and alert.

When all was ready, BRWF, with tiny Richard clinging like grim death to her chest, was quietly released onto the wall nearest to her usual roost. I had expected at least a moment's pause or some sign of uncertainty from her. However, there was no hesitation as she climbed immediately to her usual position, halting only to hook at SM who had raced over to sniff at her as she entered the higher area.

As BRWF reached her roost, the others began to converge. SM had followed her after his initial approach and was swiftly joined by BRW2, then Lucy and 010B, followed by the rest of the group. The little female was pursued by the mob into Far Quadrant 3, a lower area on the sloping roof. In spite of the vigour of their jostling pursuit, the rest showed no sign of aggression or rejection — it appeared to be a case of following rather than chasing away. They simply sniffed at her and, as he was uncovered from time to time by her movements, the baby at her breast. She maintained her position in Far Quadrant 3, hooking and occasionally vocalising at the others as they approached. By this time she seemed considerably stressed.

As far as most of the group was concerned, the novelty soon wore off. She had apparently been recognised as one of their own, although still, I imagine, with an unfamiliar whiff of the treatment centre and other smells about her. Once the others had retreated to their accustomed areas, BRWF began climbing back up towards the centre ridge to more familiar territory, only to be rushed again by the group. Still they only sniffed, dodging the hooking blows she delivered in return. She swung herself quickly down through Far Quadrant 3 and into the lowest of the roof panels adjoining the outer wall. As she moved lower, the others dropped their pursuit and returned to normal activities in the apex. I found this pattern rather interesting in the light of some evidence of altitudinal dominance, that is, the higher the roosting position, the higher the status of the bat, in other flying-foxes.

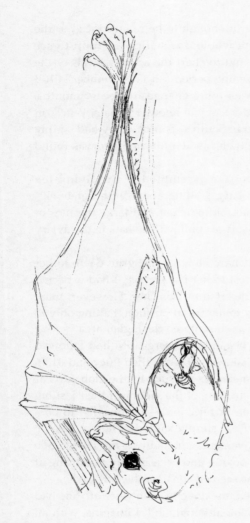

Grey-headed flying-fox (*Pteropus poliocephalus*) with young.

(See socialising young orphans chez Luckhoff on page 70, and refer to Neuweiler's study of *Pteropus giganteus* in India on pages 70, 117-8.)

All of this activity had taken place within a space of 15 minutes from the time of release. A few minutes later, BRWF began to settle to grooming herself and her infant. Peace reigned for a further minute, before SM, then Split, arrived and began sniffing, to which she responded with a shower of hooking blows until they retreated. Having held her own with the two males, a minute later she began her climb up into Far Quadrant 2, to an area within her territory, where she paused, before at last regaining her usual roost in Triangle 4.

Immediately, her neighbours' interest was renewed. BRW2, Lucy, Spot and Fang surrounded her and, after being briefly deterred by the sound of keepers' voices from somewhere outside, returned to sniff eagerly. Once again she responded with hooking and rebuff vocalisations, driving most of them away. SM and Lucy were more persistent than the others but eventually desisted and left.

After this, BRWF appeared to relax a little, briefly basking with wings pulled back to reveal the tiny dark body flattened against her, with its large head topped by black spearpoint ears and the outsized feet with long gnarled toes spreading through her belly fur, grasping tightly. Richard looked quite different to 010B's lighter-coloured, more robust female infant.

BRWF soon fell into the same pattern of wing-shielding and grooming her infant that I had observed the year before with 010 and Roger. Things were more or less as usual with the group at large, but BRW2 and 010B, normally BRWF's nearest neighbours, remained curious and approached her again. This time her reaction was more off-hand. She continued to wing-shield and attend to her offspring, hooking intermittently at the intruders, who desisted after a couple of minutes, settling to bask. For the next seven minutes peace reigned and I relaxed at last. One can be very grateful for seven minutes' respite from a sustained bout of furiously scribbling notes, shooting photographs and trying to keep at least one eye on the action all the time. There was just time to scald myself with some coffee before the bats returned to the fray.

BRWF interrupted her grooming to vocalise at 010B who had once again stalked over to her. This time it was a 'quieck' rather than the louder squawking rebuff. Soon they were joined by BRW2 and 010, who sniffed at her and Richard. The mood had changed: BRWF seemed more accepting and the others less pushy. She soon tolerated their presence as the three settled 60 centimetres to 1 metre away. BRWF enfolded Richard in her dark, soft wings and, tucking her chin into her elbow, closed her eyes.

For almost a quarter of an hour, BRWF was left to herself. The sky was now clear and the air was softened by a tinge of warmth. Apart from the occasional chiming of bell miners as they foraged somewhere outside, all was quiet. The only sign of activity amongst the resting bats was the small but energetic figure of 010B's baby, Flash, scrambling back and forth across her mother's body, suckling briefly at one breast then the other. Occasionally, a wing would unfold from the side of her light grey, gingery-ruffed body, and flap awkwardly about. Sometimes the bright-eyed pointy face would dive down from a nipple to lick quickly at her sleepy mother's muzzle.

The interlude was broken at eleven-thirty by the arrival of the usually reticent Pale to look more closely at BRWF and her young. She allowed him to within 45 centimetres of her before a hooking rebuff or warning was delivered. Then a dark form slid between them, swinging blows at the retreating Pale — it was BRW2. He stopped about 30 centimetres from BRWF and they sniffed tentatively at each other's muzzles. He ducked to sniff at her genitals and was promptly cuffed for the liberty. At that moment they were interrupted by Pale, who was again swiftly seen off by BRW2. Another hiatus followed.

From then on, it appeared that BRW2 had taken it upon himself to defend BRWF. Split, SM, Lucy and Pale made subsequent approaches at various times through the day, in each case being repelled by the intervention of BRW2. Spot was the only one he allowed to come close to BRWF, who backed down, hooking out at Spot, but was not sufficiently disturbed to stop wing-shielding and grooming Richard as she did so.

Infant grey-headed flying-fox (*Pteropus poliocephalus*).

By the end of the day, all was as usual within the colony. It was obvious that, late starter though she was, BRWF was a perfectly competent mother and unlikely to be harassed further by the others.

The following day I was able to pay more attention to comparing the two infants. Richard, at ten days old, was markedly smaller, less vigorous and less well-coordinated than 010B's Flash, who was four days old. As time went by I noticed that BRWF's mothering style was less casual than that of 010B. She was less inclined to hang open, exposing Richard and he remained less mobile than Flash. At 16 days, his head was still less mature in appearance than Flash's had been immediately after birth. His eyes were still only partially open and had a rather dull look about them.

He was 21 days old when I first saw him hanging from the wire while suckling (Flash achieved this at 16 days). There was still no coordinated wing-flapping — he moved and stretched his skinny little arms, unfolding the wrinkly dark films of membrane, but with little evidence of control.

At the end of December, when he was aged 54 days, I saw Richard away from his mother for the first time, hanging 15 centimetres from her, stretching his wings in the warm morning breeze. He was restless that day, clambering on and off his mother, sometimes licking her muzzle, sometimes just hanging as they loosely enfolded each other in a drape of flaccid wings.

In time, Richard caught up with Flash. His eyes became round and bright in his long, tapering black face and his slender pointy ears became mobile and quick to respond to every sound. In fact, my notes of 12 January, 1990 remark that although still smaller than Flash, particularly his head, he appeared to be more alert and concerned with surroundings, visitors, noises and movements than she was.

By the next mating season, Richard was sufficiently independent of BRWF for her to mate again with BRW2. The subsequent birth, although carefully supervised after some prolapsing was noticed, and attended to with a few stitches, was otherwise free from the trauma of Richard's arrival. Another dark, slender-faced male was added to the colony.

We have skidded a little ahead of proceedings in mentioning the birth of BRWF's second son, so let us return to early 1990. Towards the end of January, both Richard and Flash were shuffling away from their mothers from time to time as their strength and confidence grew. However, their mothers remained a safe 'base', as well as their source of food and warmth for some time to come. Should the mother fail to welcome her growing offspring with open wings as it were, the youngster would begin a sort of wrestling match — largely one-sided. The small wings and thumb hooks would grapple their way around the mother's neck and shoulders, the little one's head butting its way into her neck fur, ready to dive down to the maternal breast the moment her defences were breached, and fasten itself to the nipple.

I saw an interesting reflection of this infant 'neck embracing' behaviour between the adult females on one occasion. The circumstances suggested that it might serve to defuse the aggression. However, as the flying-foxes have never obliged by repeating it in my presence, I can only speculate.

Spot and 010 were within their usual territories in Triangles 1 and 2, along with Roger and SM. BRW2 was also in the vicinity, which was rather unusual. 010 moved in her accustomed slow and quiet way between her son, Roger (by now 14 months old, darker and more robust looking than his grizzled, ashy-grey little mother), and the swarthy hulk of BRW2. She was almost close enough for her back fur to brush the chest of the latter. The fray began with Roger reaching out to 010 a couple of times, causing her to shuffle around. At this point BRW2 grabbed at her so that 010, attempting to escape, moved within range of SM, who began hooking and vocalising at her. The little female backed away from him, calling and defending herself with her thumb hooks. As she moved around and away, Roger took up pursuit, sniffing and grabbing at her in a manner suggesting that an attempt at mounting was imminent — if he could just get her to stand still long enough.

Until this juncture Spot, who was being slightly buffeted by the proceedings, had ignored the whole business. Suddenly she found herself caught between the milling bats and began hooking out, hesitantly, at 010 (with whom she was normally on friendly terms), and more vigorously at the males. Suddenly 010 was behind her and Spot wheeled to hook, but appeared in a split second to recognise the offender and modify her response. Both thumbs shot out, but simply grasped 010 around the neck, holding her for a moment, then releasing her, as the youngsters commmonly grasp their mothers. Spot turned away and settled immediately. The aggressive interaction was aborted. 010 and the others also soon settled and all was quiet in the colony.

By March, the mating season was gathering momentum. In the wild, the previous season's young would have been establishing their social skills in the juvenile packs, supervised by a few unmated adults. This was, of course, impossible in the small captive colony. Roger, although, according to most authorities, too young to be sexually mature, was mating with his mother — when he could get away with it. Not that she raised much in the way of objection, but SM had taken over Scruff's little harem, to which she belonged, and he did not take kindly to sharing.

Towards the end of March, Richard was becoming increasingly venturesome and wandering about more on his own within the territory shared by his mother, BRWF, BRW2 and 010B with her offspring. One day a scuffle of wings drew my attention to BRW2, 010B and Richard trading blows and bites not far from BRWF. The action rapidly became too hot for Richard's liking and he let out the typical juvenile twitter of alarm — a high-pitched, bird-like call. To my surprise, his mother steadfastly ignored him. I had expected at least some sign of interest, if not actual protective action.

Soon after this, having been rebuffed by 010B who was typically his first choice for mating activity, BRW2 approached the still resting BRWF and began grooming her genital area. This was immediately spotted by Richard, who hurried to his mother and began beating off BRW2. In spite of the almost ludicrous disparity in size between the little russet-and-blackish aggressor and the great dark male, BRW2 retreated from Richard's onslaught without even defending himself. Mother and son were left alone. I had often been astonished by the gentleness and tolerance of the mature males when faced with the curious pokings and general

BRWF with Richard *(left)* and 010B with Flash. Both youngsters sired by BRW2.

Fang grooming Spot, her mother.

botherings of the youngsters. It reminded me of the seemingly endless patience of some silverback male gorillas I have seen in captive family groups, in particular the huge, lumbering and thoroughly forbidding presence of Matze in Frankfurt Zoo, delicately dandling even the most obnoxious of his offspring on various parts of his anatomy, allowing them to pinch, bite and explore his person to their heart's content.

As the mating season progressed into April, the division of the females amongst the males was less well defined than in the previous season. This time Split was showing more interest and activity. Although SM had more or less taken Scruff's place, there were challenges from Split. Also, the youngish female, Fang, whose tolerance of other flying-foxes began and ended with her mother, Spot, with whom she had a close, at times pseudosexual relationship, was being grabbed at by both BRW2 and SM. As was Lucy, now almost 17 months old (quite old enough to begin breeding), but inclined to run screeching from any overtures made by the males.

Fang was quite a hefty female and well able to beat off any unwelcome advances, which she did with great gusto. Spot had not had another youngster after Fang, who remained with her mother well into adulthood. I often saw them hanging huddled together, sometimes grooming each other. More usually, the grooming was performed by Fang and took the form of intensive licking around the other female's genital area, in the manner of the males before copulation. However, I never observed any attempts at mounting follow this.

I noticed a change in Roger's attitude, he was not the bumptious, socially confident bat he used to be. Since Scruff's death and SM's takeover, Roger was less inclined to assert himself. Even when well into the preliminaries of an attempted mating with his mother, he would give way without defence to the now dominant SM, which was interesting in the light of the concept of inherited social status.

Neuweiler (1962) in his study of the Indian flying-fox, observed that during the time of pair formation, a female's social status depended on that of the male with which she was associating. In some primates, the offspring in a colony will acquire their place in the hierarchy from their mother. The offspring of a dominant female may in turn dominate the subordinates of its mother. In view of the seasonal mobility of the grey-headed flying-foxes' lifestyle, it is probably unlikely that associations would continue long enough for this sort of thing to develop to any extent or to serve any purpose. But it was an interesting feature of Roger's development.

The great summer camps in the wild would mostly have broken up and dispersed in small groups to utilise scattered food resources by May. By and large only the latest crop of young, with a few adults, form sizeable winter camps. In the

Healesville colony, with adequate food on the spot and nowhere to go, they simply continued mating. This went on into June in 1990, by which time the pregnancies were already established.

The first of the females to give birth was old 010, who produced a most unusual and beautiful pale golden baby — a male, whom I named Phil. His fur reminded me of that of some of the paler specimens of golden lion tamarin I have seen. Its colour sprang gleaming to life when touched by the sunlight.

As mentioned earlier in this chapter, on 21 October BRWF gave birth to a male, Whatsit, in the off-exhibit area. Next day 010B also gave birth, to a dark, sharp-faced male (almost a replica of his half-brother Richard at that age) who later acquired the study name Kee.

The following year I was off pursuing bats, or bits of bats, in other parts of the world when the next batch of offspring arrived, thus missing most of a particularly interesting piece of business. On 20 October, keepers noted that two females had given birth in the course of the day. One mother remained unidentified, but obviously one of the males — from my observations, possibly Roger — had succeeded in impregnating Fang, as she was carrying an infant. Next morning a dead infant was found on the ground when staff arrived.

On 25 October, Spot appeared to have taken over Fang's baby. How this happened is unclear; I was away at the time and whatever transpired did so at a time when no staff were around. The baby remained with Spot until the beginning of February when I saw it back with Fang. The baby was a female, and thus something of a blessing in a group in which the ratio of males to females was becoming a concern. I called her Leonora after the heroine of one of my favourite operas, *Fidelio*. We were almost as pleased by her arrival as was Florestan, the hero of the piece, by that of his Leonora.

CHAPTER 11

Of Food
and
Digestion

Contrary to the supposition of a Dutch scoutmaster I once observed tossing pieces of bread up to the bats hanging from the wire mesh overhead, smiling happily and tweeting encouragement to them, flying-foxes are fairly restricted in their diet. Amongst the Australian pteropids, spectacled flying-foxes prefer forest fruits and the blacks and grey-headeds feed on a variety of fruits, nectar and pollen. The latter is an important source of protein in their otherwise carbohydrate-rich diet. Little reds feed predominantly on nectar and blossoms. It is interesting to compare the skulls of little reds to those of the other species and note the difference in their dentition. The teeth of the largely nectivorous little reds are smaller and often show irregularities indicating adaptive change — evolution in action.

According to Hall and Richards (1991), in northern Queensland, bee-keepers drive around at night listening for the vocalisation of little red flying-foxes. The bats are not only adept at locating flowering eucalypts, but also select the species which have the best flow of nectar. This is important to apiarists wanting to produce large amounts of honey.

The diet of flying-foxes is the key not only to their place in ecosystems, but also to their public relations problems in many places. Over the years many misconceptions have developed, and questions still remain. There are many reports of various flying-fox species as crop raiders in the notes of the colonial naturalists of the last century. Some of these are discussed in chapter 13.

In *A Monograph of Christmas Island (Indian Ocean)* edited by Charles W. Andrews (1900), a statement appears foreshadowing the message which present-day chiroptologists are at pains to emphasise. In writing of *P. natalis* on Christmas Island, it is pointed out that although it caused a great deal of destruction amongst the bananas and papayas at the settlement, when ripe wild fruits were available to them in the forests, few bats were seen to bother with the cultivated fruit in gardens.

By and large it seems that in most of the places described, a balance was struck between the bats and the village fruit growers — the bats eating some of the fruit and the villagers eating some of the bats. At times the bats got the upper hand, devastating crops of breadfruit and the like. More recently, the balance has been more seriously upset by the hunting of flying-foxes on a commercial scale.

In Australia, flying-foxes and fruit growers are traditional enemies. There are many early accounts of crops being ruined and retribution meted out by various means, which probably did more to relieve the feelings of the growers than to control flying-fox numbers or limit damage. Feelings then, and at times now, often ran high.

An account by F. G. Aflalo published in 1896 claims that the 'foetid odour' of the flying-fox is so powerful that it can render peaches unmarketable by the mere brush of a wing. Some even more colourful ideas are presented in a paper delivered to the Royal Society of Queensland by Dr Lucas, MRCSE, in the same year. He begins with some rather tame accounts of using noise to deter flying-foxes, citing the example of the natives of Viwa, Fiji, repeatedly driving away the crop raiders by beating on kerosene tins until the animals finally decamped to another island 15 miles away, where they remained.

Some of Dr Lucas's other notions are rather more intriguing. He claims that arsenic is the poison to use — in combination with finely ground white sugar it could be introduced into green fruits at random. The ripening of the treated fruit would be accelerated by the wound and the presence of foreign substances, thus offering it as the first choice of the flying-foxes. According to Dr Lucas, the first few fatalities would act as a warning and deterrent to the rest, who would then seek their meals elsewhere. He does, however, caution that foxes might carry off poisoned fruits, but suggests that this danger might be minimised by baiting only green fruit and retrieving and burning any found fallen each morning. Happily, the good doctor rejects the idea ('recommended', but by whom, he does not say) of injecting bait fruit with chicken cholera microbes.

The best solution, he cheerfully concludes, is 'organised wholesale slaughter' — taking the extermination to the flying-foxes' roosts. After describing the Aborigines' hunting methods — combining smoke with boomerangs or other missiles — Dr Lucas suggests that orchardists might combine amusement with profit and prevention by organising picnic parties to shoot out the flying-fox camps. According to his directions, fires should be lit all around the camp to stun the animals with smoke before the guns move in. Those unable to shoot, he adds, can join in these jollifications by wielding sticks and knives. He points out, presumably in the spirit of 'waste not, want not', that the skins can be used, like rat skins, for making soft leather gloves.

He then emphasises that the work must be carried out with diligence and persistence, with a view to eliminating what is referred to as a 'plague' from the land. In fact, he seems to regard these native Australian mammals in the light of airborne cane toads — claiming that they were moving inexorably northward along China's coastline where they had previously been unknown!

It is fortunate that 30 years or so later, Francis Ratcliffe's intensive and wide-ranging field studies were able to refute the dire conclusions of Dr Lucas on the subject of flying-fox management (well-received as they might still be in some quarters).

These days a good deal of work is going into investigating the conflict of interests between fruit growers and flying-foxes in Australia. Measures such as olfactory deterrents and growing of buffer crops, as well as other possibilities, are being explored. There are no simple answers. Francis Ratcliffe's pioneer study in the 1930s, described earlier in this book, concluded that firearm-fests in the flying-fox camps were not a solution.

Perhaps the most effective method of protecting crops at present is netting orchards. This is done by erecting rows of poles (similar to telegraph poles) with cables stretched between them and covering this framework with a fine-mesh nylon net. This method has the added advantages of providing some protection from bird and hail damage. This requires an initial financial outlay and is not practical in some terrain. However, enough 3.5 x 2.5-centimetre nylon mesh to cover one hectare, at a cost in the vicinity of $20 000 if installed by a contractor will, if properly maintained, last 12 to 14 years. This cost has been estimated to be recoverable within two years by some growers, if properly installed to ground level. (S. Robinson, pers. comm., 1994.)

Friends growing stone fruits on the north coast of New South Wales described to me the damage done by flying-foxes as having cost them a quarter of one year's crop. There was also some damage by brush turkeys, rosellas, bower birds and silver eyes. However, the flying-foxes stripped 300 trees of their fruit in the space of three nights, also breaking young branches and leaders in the process, thus affecting the following year's yield. Approximately 150 by 80 metres of the peach orchard has now been netted at a cost of $4000, which included the poles and cables, but no outside labour. I have since received a card, foot-noted with malicious delight, that my friends have this season enjoyed the spectacle of frustrated flying-foxes bouncing off the nets, while their fruit ripens unscathed.

Unfortunately flying-foxes have to eat. In order to do so they have, in the past, been able to migrate up and down the east coast following the flowerings and fruitings of the forests. Fragmentation of the forests has meant that there is less overall in the way of a natural dietary resource for the bats, and that those pockets remaining are too far apart to be negotiated without resorting to supplements of cultivated crops. Not all forest food is available on a predictable seasonal basis — some years are simply so hard that the flying-foxes must forage where they can.

One question, and probable misconception, which has arisen on a number of occasions is the matter of flying-foxes catching and eating fish. It is generally thought that the flying-fox's habit of skimming the surface of bodies of water to drink on the wing has given a false impression to some observers. Dr J. Shortt's letter to the Zoological Society of London in 1863, describing his observations in India, mentions that having persuaded an associate to catch a few animals in the act with the aid of his gun, he was able to confirm that the species involved was *P. edulis*. What he does not mention is any sign of fish present in the gut, mouth, claws, nor indeed secreted anywhere else about the bodies of these flying-foxes.

There are many references to flying-foxes drinking on the wing. One interesting variation is provided by R. H. Loyn in a note published in the *Victorian Naturalist* (vol. 98, no. 5, 1981) describing a colony of little red flying-foxes, gliding down over a creek, with heads held well above the water as they skimmed its surface with their bellies. Loyn then saw the animals flap off to a tree and lick up the water thus collected in their fur (shades of the African sand grouse and its water-carrying method).

In *A Natural History of the Animal Kingdom* by W. S. Dallas, FLS, (1861) readers are informed that the Kalongs of Java, *P. edulis*, have been known to eat bird flesh in captivity. He goes on to speculate whether they might also vary their fruit diet with the odd small bird in the wild. So far, I have seen no evidence of this in recent literature. Sir J. Emerson Tennent, KCS LLD &c., in his 1861 publication, *Sketches of the Natural History of Ceylon*, makes the interesting comment that the local flying-foxes 'devour' not only young birds, but birds' eggs, insects and caterpillars. Unfortunately he does not specify whether this is based on personal observation, or any reliable source. (He also notes that the Singhalese claim *Pteropus* will even attack tree snakes.) However, mention is made by Kerryn Parry-Jones and Mike Augee (1991) in an article about the diet of flying-foxes around Sydney and Gosford, of insect remains found in the faeces of *P. poliocephalus*. They also cite a report of a flying-fox seen capturing a cicada in flight.

When scanning the literature of the last century, some colourful descriptions turned up of fruit bats getting themselves well and truly legless after sampling the palm juice from the collection pots hung on trees in India. They wouldn't be the first species of wildlife to enjoy the benefits of natural fermentation. There were also sad, brief reports of the deaths of two fruit bats held by the London Zoo in its infancy. Both apparently expired, in spite of tender care and protection from draughts, their end being attributed to the cruel English climate, rather than the diet of raisins provided. Fortunately, husbandry in zoos has come a long way from the days when apes lived the high (but short) life on sausages, beer and cigars.

Peggy Eby's work on grey-headed flying-foxes and Greg Richards' on spectacled flying-foxes have shown that the flying-foxes are unique amongst seed-dispersers and pollen vectors in the wide range of their activities. Pollen, nectar and fruit are the products of forests which, through interactions with fauna, promote their own reproductive success and survival. Flying-foxes carry pollen over long distances, thus reducing the genetic isolation of species relying on pollen movement for gene flow. Greg Richards found that the spectacled flying-foxes of tropical Queensland included in their diet 26 species of native fruits from 13 families.

In his study of *P. conspicillatus,* Richards found that their diet consists of nearly 80% fruits, the rest being made up of the flowers of rainforest and sclerophyll forest trees. There is one record of foliage being eaten. (There are various reports of leaves being eaten by other flying-foxes. I have seen grey-headeds chewing at foliage, but not actually ingesting it. Kerryn Parry-Jones and Michael Augee (1991) found evidence of considereable intake of poplar and grey mangrove leaves in the droppings of grey-headed flying-foxes in the vicinity of Gosford, New South Wales.) Individuals defend feeding territories of probably about 3 metres around themselves (as Nelson found in *P. poliocephalus*). In the course of the feeding session, bats without established territories will fly in, sometimes stealing fruit before being chased away. These 'raiders', as they have been dubbed, appear to play a significant role in the dispersal of seeds.

Seeds can be dispersed by flying-foxes either internally or externally, that is, by carrying the fruit away from the parent tree. This is governed by the size of the seed and of the fruit. The largest seeds recorded in the gut were 3.7 millimetres long by 3.2 millimetres wide.

Richards collected faecal material from under *P. conspicillatus* roosts and raised seedlings from the seeds he found in it. (Seeds from the roost trees and those seeds typically wind-dispersed were excluded.) The distance they are carried internally is limited by the rate of passage of food through the gut. Tedman and Hall (1985) found that in the black and grey-headed flying-foxes this varied between 12 and 24 minutes. (Others have found longer periods of passage through the gut, depending on the material ingested.) Thus, using an estimate of a flight speed of 40 kilometres per hour, and assuming that the flying-fox made an immediate take-off after ingesting the material, the seeds could be dispersed anywhere between 8 and 22 kilometres from the parent tree. In other words, from one tract of rainforest to another. (See Appendix II on page 160.)

The role of the raiders is to carry off whole fruit from the feeding tree. Something the size of a mango can be carried in flight over a distance of approximately 100 metres, according to Richards' observations. We can speculate on the ability of bats to transport loads by relating the load to the weight of young carried in flight by females (bearing in mind the difference in loading in relation to the animal's centre of gravity, that is, unlike offspring, fruit is carried in the mouth, in front of the centre of gravity). John Nelson has observed a 700-gram grey-headed flying-fox in flight with a 400-gram youngster on board. *P. vampyrus* is reported by A. J. Marshall (1983, 1985) to be capable of carrying a 200-gram fruit in its mouth in flight.

It also appeared that the flying-foxes were more inclined to select light-coloured fruits amongst the rainforest trees, the fruits that are most readily visible under low light conditions being preferred. Richards suggests that *Pteropus* species, especially *P. conspicillatus*, are the only dispersers of seed for many of the rainforest trees.

If so, flying-foxes are an essential element in the health and survival of these forests — just as the rainforests are a key element in the bats' lifestyle and, as a primary food source, the best protection against damage to commercial crops by hungry *Pteropi*. In the light of this, it is unfortunate that flying-foxes do not enjoy government protection in Queensland at present. (Richards, 1990.)

Looking at the larger picture, fruit bats make a significant contribution to ecosystem maintenance in many parts of the world. Some of the wild plants dependent on bats include avocadoes, bananas, dates, figs, breadfruit, peaches, mangoes, carob, sisal, kapok, chicle latex, balsa and tequila. It is economically important to maintain ancestral stocks of these and other commercially grown species in the interests of finding disease-resistant genetic material and developing better varieties. Malaysia benefits to the tune of more than 100 million dollars annually from the durian crop — a fruit pollinated by fruit bats.

Australia benefits from a number of commercially exploited tree species, from black bean to bush box, for which flying-foxes act as pollinators or seed dispersers. We could also, from some points of view, such as tourism, regard the koala as an economically exploitable species. At least nine species of eucalypts and one angophora browsed by koalas are also utilised by flying-foxes.

Jeni Kendell, an independent film maker, has produced a most interesting piece entitled 'Triangle of Life', telling the story of a Samoan forest, its traditional owners and the flying-foxes. It demonstrates well the complex relationships existing between the three. She tells how Dr Paul Cox, an ethno-botanist specialising in traditional forest medicines and their pharmaceutical properties, became involved in the protection of the Falealupo rainforest in 1988.

On the island of Savaii, the chiefs of Falealupo village had been forced to sell their forests to pay for a school for the children of the island (a government ultimatum was delivered that without a new school, no teachers would be made available for Falealupo). Dr Cox offered to raise the funds to build the school if the chiefs would undertake to protect the forests in return. The arrangement duly received government approval — the rainforest would become a national park, with all commercial logging operations banned. Felling of trees would be the prerogative of villagers, for traditional uses such as house- or boat-building. This covenant would remain in force for 50 years, to allow for possible changes in the wishes of later generations.

This was a significant development in many ways. It has provided a model for other villages, at least one of which has chosen to have its forest gazetted as a national park in perpetuity. With aid from conservationists in other countries, tens of thousands of hectares of Samoa's forests have been secured for the future in accordance with the wishes of its people.

As far as the Falealupo agreement is concerned the implications benefit both people and wildlife — in fact, the two are bound intimately by the very nature of rainforests. These forests are now often referred to as 'nature's pharmacy', already having yielded the primary ingredients for many solutions to medical problems. Much more lies in wait of discovery, if indeed the forests survive long enough for this to happen. In Falealupo it was agreed that the village community would receive a portion of the royalties due on any such commercially viable discoveries in their forest.

For the forests to remain healthy it is necessary to do more than just stop cutting them down. Thus, it was appropriate that the flying-foxes *Pteropus samoensis* also received protection. After years of pressure from hunting, numbers were dwindling (see chapter 13). Along with *P. tonganus*, these bats, as pollinators, play a vital role in rainforest regeneration. It is a sad thought that the rate of decline of the forests in some islands of the Pacific might outstrip the need for protecting the flying-foxes. If the forests dwindle for lack of pollinators, the bats themselves become biologically irrelevant.

After so much about what flying-foxes feed on and the ecological implications, it is probably time to get back to the more basic matter of how the animals deal with what they eat. When studying the gastro-intestinal tracts of black and grey-headed flying-foxes, Les Hall and R. A. Tedman found that the time taken for food to pass through the digestive tract was remarkably short for animals of that size (this has already been mentioned above). This has the advantage of making energy rapidly available without the need for a full digestive tract to hamper the animal in flight during the night's foraging. Tedman and Hall found that the stomachs of both species are well developed in those areas where food is attacked by hydrochloric acid: the cardiac and fundic regions. The comparatively large microvilli — the finger-like projections lining the intestines — provide an extended surface area through which nutrients can be absorbed.

As already mentioned, pollen is an important element in the flying-foxes' diet. However, the proteins within pollen grains are not readily available, being covered by a coating which prevents easy access. However, they are not impregnable, and have been shown to open when immersed in a warm solution of sugar and water. Just such a solution is provided by a fruit bat's saliva, mixed with the nectar being ingested along with the pollen. (Mohr, 1976.) Burst pollen grains have even been found in the fur around the shoulders of flying-foxes, presumably where the animals have been grooming with saliva during or immediately after feeding. (M. McCoy, pers. comm., 1990.) Pollen grains thus breached are then vulnerable to the hydrochloric acid secretion of the stomach which dissolves out the protein, making it available for digestion and absorption lower in the gut.

The long, pointed tongue of the flying-fox is also interestingly adapted to its diet. Even in the newborn young, the upper surface of the tongue is covered with sharply pointed backward-facing scales (see diagram) which assist the animal in a multitude of ways: drinking; feeding (the tongue movements in nectar- and blossom-feeding are comparable to those of lorikeets); compacting fruit and rupturing pollen grains against the ridges of the hard palate; grooming; sexual grooming of the female genitalia by males and nipple attachment and milk extraction by infants. (L. Martin, pers. comm., 1994.)

The scales covering the surface of the tongue assist in feeding and drinking.

CHAPTER 12

Bats
and
Humans

T he non-evolutionary relationships between humans and bats in general are complex and widely varying. This applies to whole cultures as well as individual reactions. It is easy to make sweeping statements along the lines of Western culture being historically anti-bat, whilst the Chinese and other Oriental cultures regard them as symbols of good fortune. In China, a bat flying into the house signifies that good luck will enter the house; in Europe, the same event signifies death. In Greek mythology bats accompanied spirits to Hades.

Spending so many hours in a cage full of bats to which the public has access, I have heard all sorts of comments, many of which cannot simply be classified as either positive or negative. Some vehemently negative attitudes change when the person who has arrived loaded with traditional Western cultural baggage clouding his or her vision actually makes eye contact with a bat for the first time, or watches the interactions between the flying-foxes. When the myth gets out of the way and the animal can be seen as something of flesh and blood to which we can relate, and which reacts to — even acknowledges us — the human reaction is almost invariably positive.

Perhaps the types of bat commonly encountered and their more pragmatic roles in human societies affect cultural attitudes and the attendant mythologies. It is interesting to wonder whether a line drawn around the 'bat-positive' parts of the world would correspond roughly to the distribution of the Megachiroptera.

In Europe the microchiropterans remain creatures of mystery, inhabitants of dark and, from the human viewpoint, uninviting places. They live on the fringes of human existence — either in the dark of night or in their inaccessible roosts — and are thus more in the human imagination than are more familiar animals. Their tiny shapes flit about too quickly to be properly seen or touched, they are beyond our control . . . perhaps in the same way that spiders scuttling swiftly, unpredictably, on too many legs, give the impression that they could at any moment land on one's person. The insectivorous bats for the most part lack the facial features to which humans naturally respond, having small insignificant eyes, large mouths with needley teeth (often gaping, not to intimidate, but to echolocate) and often strangely wrinkled or leaved muzzles. The delicate, exquisitely furred bodies are visually overpowered by the strange membranous leather of the wings, which are neither furred nor feathered for the comfort of our mind's eye, which favours the familiar.

In parts of the world where fruit bats are more common, the attitude is different. These bats often live out in the open, roosting in trees and socialising in broad daylight. Their eyes are large and bright, their faces reminiscent of the dogs that share intimately in humans' day-to-day lives. There is a familiarity about them — they are large and furry enough to be seen properly and recognised as mammals like us. In many places they are important food items, something bound to incline people to a more prosaic attitude. The relationship between these bats and the rest of their world can be seen at a very basic level, by watching them eat and distribute the seeds of forest fruits. In the *Book of Indian Animals*, S.H. Prater mentions that there are parts of India where the flying-foxes carry seed (in fruit or in their droppings) in sufficient quantities to their colonial roosts that the rights to collecting it from the ground beneath were rented annually.

The flying-fox is a part of day-to-day life, even a part of the figurative language in some areas of Polynesia. In Fiji, where it is known as 'mbeka', a person given to sketchy bathing habits may be referred to as 'boiboi vaka mbeka', comparing his body odour to that of a bat. 'Samusamu mbeka' suggests that someone idles about like a bat; likewise, 'kanakana vaka mbeka' (eat like a flying-fox) may be applied to someone whose manners leave much to be desired. (Hill and Smith, 1984.) All this, although not particularly complimentary from the flying-fox's point of view, at least implies its acceptance as an integral part of living, something to which human behaviour relates, rather than an unseen horror from the realms of darkness and mystery.

It has been suggested that the Chinese view of the bat as a symbol of good fortune has a similar origin. Before the peach tree was cultivated in China about 5000 years ago, the wild form was dependent on fruit bats for seed dispersal — to 'spread its descendants'. Hence, apparently, the ancient Bat and Peach symbol of abundant descendants and good fortune or longevity. (Chang Chin-ju, 1992. Sinorama.) More of that and the roles of bats in traditional Chinese medicine later.

Perhaps, inevitably, attitudes to bats are changing. As with many other things, the cultures of East and West are beginning to flavour one another. As Batman invades Asia, Europe has had its Year of the Bat, encouraging chiropteran appreciation. Above all, our understanding of the world and the biological role of bats has grown. Societies for the study and conservation of bats have been established around the world (see Appendix 3 on page 161); people are encouraged to provide nest boxes or preserve natural roosts for bats rather than fumigating their houses to banish them. Bats are being widely accepted as part of the scheme of things and part of our lives. However, a good deal of mystery and unfamiliarity remains.

When we think of urban mammals — animals that commonly live at close quarters with us — bats are rarely mentioned. In Melbourne, perhaps some people would cite the grey-headed flying-foxes that live in the Botanic Gardens; and feed in suburban gardens. Not many people know that they are not the only bats using the Botanic gardens, Lindy Lumsden of the Arthur Rylah Institute has also trapped bent-winged bats, *Miniopterus schreibersii*, there. In fact we share the Melbourne area with Gould's wattled bat (*Chalinolobus gouldii*), the little forest eptesicus (*Eptesicus vulturnus*), the lesser long-eared bat (*Nyctophilus geoffroyi*) and the white-striped mastiff bat (*Tadarida australis*). Moving away from the inner suburbs, the list grows longer. In spite of this, most people are unaware of their presence, let alone their activities.

Even living in a fairly bat-rich country area, I seldom see or hear evidence of their presence. After twenty-something years in my house, the first visit by a bat occurred only recently. I was woken in the wee small hours by a dry fluttering sound, rapidly approaching and retreating. Struggling to consciousness, it occurred to me that perhaps this was a dream brought on by reading *Nightwing* by Martin Cruz Smith, a lurid fantasy about hordes of vampire bats laying waste to man and beast. As Kenneth my cat sprang from apparent coma to bristling attention — as cats do — I realised there was actually a bat in the room. Logic argued that it couldn't be — all the windows and doors were tightly closed — but as the cat leapt from the bed, so did I, more or less.

The kitchen light had been left on and I saw the twin silhouettes of bat and cat sail airborne through the hallway. Almost in slow motion, the cat's slender, sinewy form arched backwards, elongating in midair as a paw extended upward, tapping the bat out of its flight path. Almost as if it had lost its balance, the bat tumbled gracefully down, gliding to rest under the dining table. Kenneth simply sat down with what at that time of night looked like a condescending smile, allowing me to crawl under the table and retrieve the prize. It was a lesser long-eared bat. As I held the impossibly delicate pulsating body, examining it for evidence of injury, I found it difficult to relate this to the strong, squawking handfuls of *Pteropus* I was used to. As it seemed quite unhurt, I opened a window and watched the tiny bat flit into the darkness. I have yet to discover how it managed to infiltrate the house.

Until dawn I lay awake, thinking about this extraordinary interlude. Those initial waking moments had for the first time enabled me to understand the early confusion that reigned over the place of bats in nature. On re-creating in my mind that fast-flying, sharp-winged shape first glimpsed in the half light, I was reminded of the flight of swallows and martins. It was quite different to the impression gained by watching bats fly when one has deliberately set out to do so. The confusion over the affiliations of bats perhaps has contributed to the lack of acceptance in some areas.

Bats have often been regarded as birds, from the earliest times down to the middle of the 17th century or, in some cases, as in that of Plato, as neither bird nor beast. Ray, the eminent zoologist, was the first (1683) who placed them in their proper position amongst the mammals, where, according to modern naturalists, they form a distinct order. Significantly, it was in the *Natural History of Birds*, published in 1740, that bats were divided into a number of distinct species. (Robertson, 1990.)

One of Aesop's fables, elegantly retold in verse by La Fontaine, tells of a weasel catching a bat and before devouring it, mentioning that he eats only mice. The bat replies that it is a bird, displaying its wings as evidence. Later the same bat is caught by another weasel, a hater of birds. The bat this time persuades his attacker that he is in fact a mouse, displaying his lack of feathers as proof.

This theme is reflected in Polynesian mythology. In a story originating from the island of Niue, war broke out between the birds and beasts in which the flying-fox alternated loyalties by exploiting its characteristics according to which side appeared to be winning. Its ambivalence was rewarded in the end with rejection from both birds and beasts, to which is attributed the fruit bats' nocturnal and separate lifestyle. (Sinavaiana & Enright, 1992.)

The Bible speaks of the bat in Deuteronomy xiv. 18 and Leviticus xi. 19, along with the stork, the heron and their like, and the hoopoe as one of the fowls that may not be eaten. In the subsequent verse of Leviticus the bat is included amongst 'fowls that creep, going upon all four' or in some translations, 'Every winged four-footed thing which goes on the earth is disgusting to you'. Not promising for the future of chiropteran public relations.

I find it interesting that although the bat is classified here with the birds on the basis of its wings, the emphasis is on the terrestrial aspect of its lifestyle. It is also referred to elsewhere in the Bible as being in the company of moles, inhabiting holes and cavities and ruins, where man casts his idols of silver and gold 'to the moles and to the bats; to go into the clefts of the rock and into the tops of the ragged rock'. (Isaiah II. 20, 21.)

In spite of the Old Testament taboo on the eating of bats, megachiropterans are popular items of diet in a number of cultures. In Australia, *Pteropus* species were eaten by the Aborigines, who would smoke them in the roost trees to stupefy them, then knock them down with some missile or other. There are various accounts from settlers, explorers and voyagers . . . 'The flying-fox (*P. conspicillatus*) is caught and eaten by the natives of northern Australia. The flesh is said to be very good. On some of the islands the bats appear in prodigious numbers, and they may be seen flying in the bright sunshine, a thing unusual in nocturnal animals.' (*Voyage of HMS Rattlesnake*, 1852, vol. 1, p. 97.) Flying-foxes also provided the expedition of the explorer Leichhardt with a few meals en route to Port Essington.

Colonial housewives also made use of the local wildlife. A certain Mrs Lance Rawson included a flying-fox recipe in her Australian cookbook and cheerfully assured her readers that minus wings and skin, one would hardly know them from pork. She recommends cutting up the flying-foxes and stewing them for a couple of hours with an onion and a variety of herbs, before turning out into a pie dish and covering with a good pastry. Curried, she claims, flying-fox is indistinguishable from pork. (Allen, G. M., 1939.)

Over the years I have collected a number of recipes for flying-foxes from various sources. One was even created for me by a friend who trained as a chef in Taiwan. He theorised from the descriptions of the flavour and texture of flying-fox flesh in my notes and created a marvellous dish garnished with black mushrooms and dried chestnuts. I frequently experiment with my pteropid recipe collection, using a variety of substitutes for bat meat. I have read and heard of flying-fox flesh being likened to that of a wide range of animals, including partridge, chicken, hare, pig (might one assume that as echidna meat has also been described as resembling pork, that flying-foxes taste like spiny anteaters?) and others. Unlike the gentleman being prosecuted for killing and eating a platypus, who was surreptitiously asked by the judge how it tasted, and answered, 'Somewhere between koala and dolphin meat', I am unable to offer an opinion.

In 1861, Tennent wrote that *P. giganteus* was killed and eaten by the natives of Ceylon, the flesh being likened by one who had tried it to that of a hare.

(Allen, op. cit.) *Pteropus giganteus* has also featured in the cuisine of a number of areas in India. Dodsworth observed in 1914 that cages of flying-foxes were to be seen in the Calcutta livestock market, where they were much sought after by the Chinese as a delicacy. (Allen, op. cit.) Various *Pteropus* species are eaten in Borneo, Java and the Philippines, or at least used to feature in the diet of natives in those islands. *P. vampyrus* from Timor was earlier christened *P. edulis* in deference to its gastronomic qualities. (Hill and Smith, 1984.)

I was told by a visitor to the Healesville Sanctuary's flying-foxes of a restaurant he had visited in Johore Bahru, Malaysia, where flying-fox curried with vegetables was on the menu. In Indonesia, the large flying-foxes are known as 'kalongs' and are eaten in curries, amongst other things. Amongst some recipes sent to me by Chris Tideman of the Australian National University is Kalong Rendang, in which the bats are cooked with coconut milk and a mixture of turmeric, chilli, onion, rock salt, coriander, cumin, ginger and garlic.

In Samoa, 'manu lagi' (the animal of the heavens) was eaten when it came to feed on the breadfruit crops (a retaliatory tactic which has so far not occurred to Australian fruit growers, it appears). The method of capture was to attach a prickly bush to a long pole and strike the flying-fox with it, thus entangling the wings. (Allen, 1939.)

Similarly, on Aneitum Island, where two *Pteropus* species, *P. aneitianus* and *P. geddiei* occur; the latter, more common, species itself became an item of the villagers' diet when it came to raid their breadfruit crops twice a year. Macgilvray (1860) described how they were trapped in circular, flat-bottomed baskets resembling fish traps, open at the top and baited with pawpaw.

The culinary merit of *Pteropus edwardsii* in the Seychelles, where it was popular with the Creole people, is summed up for us by E. P. Wright. According to his 1868 account, its dark flesh made good eating, provided that the animal was skinned within minutes of its death and roasted on the same day. (Allen, op. cit.)

In the highlands of New Guinea, fossilised remains of fruit bats have been found in kitchen middens as old as 10 to 12 000 years. The animals appear in large enough accumulations to suggest that they were significant items in the diet of the tribes of the area. The species involved are *Dobsonia moluccensis* (a medium-sized fruit bat known as bare-backed because of the naked wing membranes which meet in the middle of its back), *Rousettus stresemanni* (a smaller species) and a species for which a new genus was created by James Menzies in 1977, *Aproteles bulmerae*. (*Aproteles* is derived from the Greek signifying incompleteness at the front, which is a reference to its lack of lower front teeth, and *bulmerae* is an acknowledgement of archaeologist Susan Bulmer, who discovered the species in the course of her excavations.)

Flying-foxes help pollinate some of the trees on which koalas feed, keeping forests healthy.

Green ring-tailed possums (*Pseudocheirus archeri*) share the north Queensland rainforests with the flying-foxes.

Otherwise known as Bulmer's fruit bat, the species was thought to have become extinct at the end of the Ice Age, about 9000 years ago. However, two years after the description was published, an anthropologist, David Hyndman, was collecting animals hunted by the Wopkaimin people in the Hindenburg Ranges in far western Papua New Guinea and sent a group of specimens to Menzies for identification. Amongst them were two skulls and two mandibles belonging to Bulmer's fruit bats — the species was not extinct. However, still no skin was available, as the one prepared and mounted by Hyndman had gone astray on the way to Port Moresby. (Menzies, 1977; Hyndman and Menzies, 1980.)

Subsequent visits to the cave were discouraging. In 1977, Hyndman found only two bats in residence and Menzies did not find any in 1985, probably due to the activities of hunters equipped with shotguns. Bulmer's fruit bat was once more presumed extinct. Perhaps it should be rechristened the Lazarus bat. In the early 1990s, Dr Tim Flannery of the Australian Museum and Lester Seri of the Papua New Guinea Department of Environment and Conservation decided to make one more attempt at the site on the grounds that some specimens, which proved to have been collected in the mid-1980s, turned up in the collections of the Australian Museum. This time, after risking life and limb to set their net in the tree canopy above the cave, inconveniently located on the edge of a limestone plateau ending at an escarpment more than a kilometre high, they were able to introduce a living, breathing *Aproteles bulmerae* to science. They had discovered a colony of around 130 individuals. (Flannery, 1993.)

Bulmer's fruit bat appears to be just one of the species whose survival is affected by human population pressure, with the attendant increase in hunting for food, exacerbated by the advent of a growing human population armed with modern weapons in areas where previously less efficient methods regulated the numbers that could be killed. Breakdown of cultural taboos may also be a factor, as suggested by Flannery.

On Guam, Saipan and Rota Islands, flying-foxes are a featured delicacy in the local Chamorro cuisine. They are eaten stewed in coconut milk. Hunting pressure has kept numbers low on Guam since the 1920s and the availability of modern firearms since the Second World War has hastened their decline.

There are probably about 600 *Pteropus mariannus* remaining on Guam, although they remain fairly common on most of the ten islands north of Saipan. After fluctuating between several thousand in 1958 and about 70 individuals in 1978, the population on Guam had recovered somewhat by 1982, reaching approximately 1000 (perhaps including immigrant animals from Rota). However, when illegal hunting increased in 1983 and 1984, numbers dropped back to around five hundred. Should flying-foxes disappear entirely from Guam, the implications for its forest could prove disastrous. At least 40% of the tree species involved are reliant on the bats for seed dispersal. (BCI; IUCN SSC Trade Specialist Group; Wiles, 1987; Wiles, 1992.)

There was a second species of flying-fox endemic to Guam, *P. tokudae*. The last known inidividual was shot by a hunter in 1968 — it is now presumed to be extinct. Following the limitations placed on hunting flying-foxes on Guam, the importation of them from other islands such as Yap and Palau increased. By the late 1970s the importation of flying-foxes from various sources around the Marianas and Caroline Islands into Guam had peaked at 20to 29 000 per annum. They were a major commodity. In the mid-1980s, there was a change in the major sources, with Western Samoa, Palau, American Samoa, Tonga, Papua New Guinea and the Philippines being the main suppliers. Since 1981, Guam's import numbers have waned to an estimated 13 500 per year. In Samoa, the harvesting of flying-foxes for the export market is a matter of individual enterprise, rather than a generally accepted commercial activity. According to Sinavaiana and Enright (1992), the selling of flying-foxes is regarded by the community at large as a disgraceful and criminal activity. They add that the bats are eaten as a delicacy in Samoa, but not as a 'feast food'. However, the popularity of *Pteropus* in the cooking pots of Guam has had wide-reaching effects throughout the region.

As an interesting sideline to the issue of fruit bats as marketable culinary commodities, a letter appeared in the periodical *Nigerian Field* in 1975, informing readers that the University of Ife Fruit Bat Project was able to be entirely financially self-supporting, an unusual distinction for a research project. This is a consequence of the popularity of its subject as a local food item. The species is not named in the letter but the writers recommend the use of six bats to serve four people as a 'light meal' — each bat weighing about 1.3 to 1.8 kilograms. However, in the recipe cited for Bat Stew, one bat per person is regarded as adequate — presumably as onions and tomatoes are added. There is a note of caution in the stew recipe that when gutting the animals any uterus containing an embryo should be thrown away as it is inadvisable for pre-menopausal women to view such things.

There is also a recipe for Roast Bat, which involves drying the bats over glowing coals for three days, after which they can be stored for several days and fried or stewed as required. The third recipe is intriguingly titled 'Expat' Bat. This involves two sessions of boiling followed by frying, stewing or roasting at the chef's discretion. Whether or not one fancies the dishes, it shows an enterprising approach to research funding. Someone more shameless than I might suggest that it might provide food for thought for Len Martin's team and their flying-fox colony at the University of Queensland.

Even that stalwart of Australian domesticity, the *Australian Women's Weekly* (the January 1820 issue to which I refer carrying the subtitle 'The Colony's Brightest Magazine') does its bit to popularise the flying-fox in its drive to share 'receipts' using local animals and produce amongst its readers. (It also notes that receipts are 'now often called "recipes" by the less educated'!) The recommendation is that flying-foxes should be eaten during the fruit season as they acquire a peculiar taste from some flower or foliage in their diet at other times. The article goes on to describe the flesh as, 'clean and white, looking somewhat like a fowl that has been skinned', and suggests stuffing with breadcrumbs or herbs before roasting or boiling the animal. As an afterthought the ladies of the colony are informed that, 'A young flying-fox split like a Spatch cock [sic] and grilled is a capital breakfast dish.'!

More recently, the *Sydney Morning Herald* has made its contribution. In July 1990, Mary Louise O'Callaghan wrote of the gastronomic charms of New Caledonia and Vanuatu, mentioning that although flying-foxes are protected in the former, there is a restaurant in the capital, Noumea, where the Volaille du Chef that occasionally appears as *plat du jour* has never needed plucking. She describes how French gourmets in search of a legitimate *Rousette au Vin* — flying-fox cooked with lemon juice and red wine — must travel to Port Vila, where the restrictions do not apply. The bats may also be cooked in an oven, wrapped in banana leaves, or rather more imaginatively eaten as Potted Bat, a rillette cooked with juniper berries.

Perhaps surprisingly, the traditional Chinese concern with bats, including flying-foxes is more medicinal than culinary. In the *Pen-Ts'ao Kang Mu*, an ancient Chinese materia medica, they are yet again categorised amongst the birds. The flesh of the flying-fox is said to be 'sweet, warming and non-poisonous. To be eaten as a general tonic'. The dried dung of the flying-fox was used in classical prescriptions such as Shih Hsiao San which 'cures the sickness and produces smiles'. The dung was thought to be a circulatory stimulant 'entering the liver very rapidly' and that some common eye diseases were best treated by improving this. For snake bite in cases where 'the patient has been unconscious for a long time' the internal use of a mixture of two parts flying-fox dung with one part antimony sulphide 'rubbed up with wine and decanted' was recommended, along with the external application of the residue to the site of the bite 'with instant effect and with return of consciousness'. It was said to be a 'blood medicine' which acted on the peripheral and central circulatory system and cured all kinds of pain. The list of applications is long. (Read, 1932.)

The ancient Egyptians, Arabs, Syrians and Indians, amongst others, found uses for the bits and pieces of various bats as medicine, cosmetics, hair dye, a depilatory for the eye lashes and elsewhere, as well as hair restorer. In parts of India, flying-fox skins or fat are a traditional poultice for the relief of rheumatism.

The fat is also thought useful for preventing baldness. In some areas it is believed that a bone from the wing of a flying-fox bound to a woman's ankle with hair from a black cow's tail will effectively banish the pain of childbirth. In the Torres Strait Islands I was told that flying-fox flesh and fat are used to combat respiratory disorders.

It is usually cited that the oldest recognised depictions of bats date back to around 2000 BC. These were painted on the tomb walls at Beni Hasan during the twelfth dynasty in Egypt. The species involved are possibly *Rousettus aegypticus* and *Taphozous perforatus*. However, these are probably considerably pre-dated by the flying-foxes represented in Australian Aboriginal rock art.

Bats have also appeared, from ancient times, as a constant theme and in varying degrees of stylisation, in Chinese art. As a rule their role is symbolic, as mentioned at the beginning of this chapter. The theme is a pun on the word *Fu*, which means good fortune as well as bat. Hence the well-known symbol of the *Wu* (5) *Fu* representing health, happiness, longevity, contentment and prosperity (or good health, longevity, wealth, virtue and a peaceful natural death — the latter often coyly avoided these days). The wing shape of a bat in flight has also had its influence, resembling, as it does with some imagination, the traditional cloud-scroll symbol, which is considered lucky. When a bat is combined in a rebus with a peach and a pomegranate, it represents many descendants and good fortune.

In Ancient China, before the Shou and Chou dynasties, the bat was the animal totem of a clan, and regarded by that race as an ancestral symbol and guardian spirit. The significance of the bat as a symbol spread throughout China during the Han Dynasty. (Chang Chin-Ju, Sinorama, August 1992.)

After many trips to Hong Kong concerned with other matters, in 1991 I decided to devote most of my time to tracking down examples of bats in art and artefacts. It was a fascinating exercise which soon developed the proportions of an obsession. I was beginning to see bats everywhere. The most interesting aspect, from a personal perspective, was that as my eyes grew accustomed to the variety of bat symbols and particularly those stylised almost beyond recognition from the more literal interpretations, I could identify bat motifs on things I had been looking at for years, all unknowing. They appeared on brocades and embroideries, in teacups and rice bowls, embossed or painted on the backs of hand mirrors, on cloisonné pill boxes, ceramics, brasses and antique jade thumb rings; even in the carvings which had stared down over many years as I made cups of coffee in the kitchen of the home of the friends I stayed with.

So much that was familiar was suddenly revealed in greater depth. What I had earlier seen as a part of China's past in the art and carvings seen in various parts of the mainland appeared almost wherever I looked in modern Hong Kong. I felt I should go back to China with newly opened eyes.

China was, however, temporarily out of the question. It was time to apply myself more energetically to my own artistic representation of bats. In spite of the surfeit of symbolic bats I had seen, the influence on my own paintings came from a different source in Hong Kong. Since my first visit in the late 1970s, I had been much taken with a metal (copper, I think) mural in the Princes Building in Central. Its heavily textured surface and subtle verdigris tonings had been one of those lurking inspirations for years. Now I knew how to direct it — it was to solve the problem of how to represent the complex folds and textures of the flying-foxes' wings. Paint alone would not give the subtle strength and patina-effect I was looking for. I discarded the idea of actually using copper foil collaged onto the paper or silk, as the contrast between that and the soft painted areas would have been too harsh. Eventually the answer came to me as I was mummifying a few food scraps to be relegated to the back of the refrigerator — plastic kitchen wrap! It would stretch and crinkle into just the effects I was after and would take the layers of paints and varnishes I had in mind for the semi-metallic finishes. Thus I entered another major phase of my association with flying-foxes.

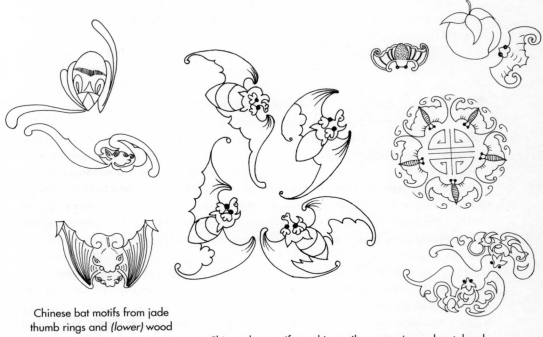

Chinese bat motifs from jade thumb rings and *(lower)* wood carvings.

Chinese bat motifs used in textiles, ceramics and metalwork.

CHAPTER 13

A Bat Hunt
with a
Difference

Tepid water lapped at my knees, its soft gurgling echoing faintly in the darkly humid air. Occasionally a sharp crack and splash resounded somewhere in the blackness as a piece of rock detached itself from above and joined the slippery fragments shifting beneath my feet. Instinctively my toes attempted to grip through the thin plastic of my sandals as I gingerly tottered along, trying to remain vertical and silent. A coolly slimy tangle of sticks and weeds brushed my leg as it floated along, spinning in slow motion, on the current. Ahead of me a dim red light moved and a voice whispered, 'By the way, try to dodge those little floating islands if you can — I quite often find cobras and kraits hitching rides on them.'

The voice was that of Gary Ades, authority on the bats of Hong Kong, who had recently taken on the task of identifying the species and locations of the colony's chiropterans. Assisted by a grant from the World Wildlife Fund, Hong Kong, Gary produced an excellent booklet, *Bats of Hong Kong*, providing a long-overdue clarification of bat species present and the problems facing them. This had been sent to me by Sue Earle, wildlife photographer, writer and, as a mutual friend appreciatively put it, hostess extraordinaire. One of the more exciting discoveries we made in the course of this research was that the small fruit bat, *Rousettus leschenaultii*, previously recorded only once in Hong Kong and assumed to be a 'blow in', was, in fact, to be found as a colony residing in a tunnel in the New Territories.

This tunnel, one of a number threading unobtrusively through and around the hills in a series of concrete-lined conduits bringing water from mainland China to the New Territories, was where my naturalist's curiosity was doing battle with a natural coward's instincts. Although, frankly, the chance of encountering venomous reptiles bothered me less than the prospect of the 6.5-metre climb up a slippery metal ladder set into the vertical concrete wall of the mouth of the tunnel. Even a steep staircase is sufficient to make me distinctly uncomfortable. I also wondered quietly about what 'only shallow water' might mean coming from someone of Gary's considerable height and length of leg. These things concern 157-centimetre non-swimmers. I had been on too many field trips to believe the smiling reassurances of any zoologist hellbent on finding an animal. Of course, it had also occurred to me that one of those falling rock fragments chancing to connect with one's skull might render all other concerns irrelevant.

Now and then we stopped while Gary made broad sweeps with a hand net through the heavy air. The first catch was a lesser bent-winged bat, *Miniopterus australis*, a tiny insectivore also found in Australia. It was soon followed by two species of *Myotis*: the large mouse-eared bat, *M. myotis*, and *M. ricketti*, with its characteristically large feet. In the distance a point of light could be seen in the gloom, where the tunnel at last emerged on the far side of the hill. That was where we expected to see the Rousettes if, indeed, they were still using the roost. We tried to go even more quietly, gliding, at times awkwardly, as loose rocks tipped beneath our feet, upsetting the balance carefully maintained against the current that was running strongly in the deeper spots. In the dim red light of Gary's torch we could just discern the bodies of minuscule *Hipposideros*, clinging to the craggy vault above us or falling into rapid, dodging flight like shadows. It was impossible to tell whether the sounds coming to us from the distant entrance were the vocalisations of *Rousettus* or merely the chattering of water upon rock.

Gradually the unrelieved darkness of the mid-section gave way to a hazy twilight and silhouetted against the disc of bright day now glowing nearer, we watched the larger bodies of Rousettes sweeping in front of us and out into the hot afternoon air, to disappear amongst the tangle of forest covering the hillside. At least we knew they were still using the tunnel. Rather than disturbing them any further, we backtracked through the resounding cavern, the whisper of wings now

Black baza (*Aviceda leuphotes*) — a bat predator in Hong Kong.

and then ruffling the air around our heads as one of the smaller bats swooped from its roost.

Whatever small disappointment there might have been at not seeing *Rousettus* face to face fled as I goaded myself back up the ladder with the thought that I should soon meet the bat I had been after for some years. Clinging to the metal rungs, knees atremble, I closed my eyes and thought of *Cynopterus* — and climbed.

Half an hour later, glaring at me from Gary's cotton-gloved hand, was a small, delicate creature that is surely one of nature's greater works of art. The short fine fur of *Cynopterus sphinx sphinx*, the dog-faced fruit bat, is a softly muted cocoa brown, with a gentle flush of gold suffusing the mantle around its shoulders. The large eyes are a rich, lively brown. Tracing the delicate lines of the wing bones and ear rims are fine lines of white, contrasting sharply with the soft darkness of the membranes.

Some years before, I had noticed a Java apple (*Sizygium*) fruiting in the Hong Kong Zoological and Botanical Gardens, where I was, as usual, making drawings of the select but opulent collection of birds and mammals before the heat of the day set in. There is usually a race between the pen and the torrid, sodden grey heat of typhoon weather, or the torrents of fat, warm rain flung like bathwater over the island. It says much for the generosity of spirit of my friends in Hong Kong that their hospitality has continued in spite of the regular appearance of out-of-season typhoons the moment I arrive in the colony. One of them, Dr Ken Searle, is the Honorary Zoological Curator (and to a large extent creator) of the Hong Kong Zoological and Botanical Gardens and it was his casual remark that the Java apples were a source of food for some wild fruit bats living in the gardens, that cost me many hours of frustration and many florid, festering bites from the particularly savage mosquitoes that also haunt the damp green slopes.

The favourite roost of *Cynopterus sphinx sphinx* is the Chinese fan palm (*Livistona chinensis*). They efficiently convert the fronds into 'tents' by biting through the rib of each leaf blade, causing a fringe of leaves to collapse around the central area where up to seven or so bats can shelter. Although I eventually succeeded in finding bat tents in the gardens, the animals themselves remained elusive.

On returning to Hong Kong later in 1991, guided once again by Gary Ades, I was at last able to see wild *Cynopterus* — living, appropriately, in the garden of Island House, World Wide Fund for Nature Hong Kong's Conservation Studies Centre in the New Territories. Originally built on a small island, Yuen Chau Tsai, a rocky outcrop in the shallows of Tolo Harbour, Island House was to house officers and servants of the Magistracy and Land Office. By the time the building was completed in 1906, an embankment constructed during the

The dog-faced fruit bat (*Cynopterus sphinx sphinx*).

creation of a road along the Tai Po shoreline formed a causeway linking the island to the mainland. This has long since been overwhelmed by land reclamation. Island House, although somewhat isolated by Hong Kong standards, is now a part of the mainland. After being occupied by a succession of district commissioners, in 1986 the house was made available to the World Wide Fund for Nature Hong Kong. Today it is becoming an island once more — an island of vegetation in a bleached grey sea of concrete, as urban development engulfs the land.

The two-storey red brick and roughcast house, with its rather fanciful cement imitations of timber framing, stands in a hilltop garden fringed with tall trees and huddles of fan palms. Watching the small dark knots of bodies high overhead in their emerald-bladed tents, I wondered how much longer *Cynopterus* could be regarded as a successful example of urban adapted wildlife in Hong Kong.

In 1966 a paper by P. M. Marshall and F. O. P. Hechtel published in the *Memoirs of the Hong Kong Natural History Society* describes *Cynopterus sphinx sphinx* as 'fairly common'. However, Hong Kong has in the meantime undergone extensive urban development which has seen the disappearance of former roosting locations, as well as both wild and cultivated feeding areas (for example, banana plantations). (G. Ades, pers. comm., 1991.) It seems that like many other bats, *Cynopterus* can exist alongside human populations, provided that the basic requirements of food and roosting sites are met.

Many species, for example those already mentioned inhabiting the man-made water tunnels, can exploit various forms of artificial shelter (roof cavities, disused mines and the like) in the absence of adequate natural sites. In a recent issue of *Porcupine!*, newsletter of the Hong Kong University Ecology Research Group, Hubert Merz reports having seen a group of minuscule Japanese pipistrelles (*Pipistrellus abramus*) leaving an air-conditioning unit located in the wall of the sixteenth floor of an apartment building! Provided these roost sites receive adequate protection from human interference, all is well. Vulnerable areas, such as the water tunnels, can be fairly easily protected by the installation of sturdy metal grilles. In the case of buildings, due care must be taken to avoid the use of insecticides and fungicides, also toxic to bats, if a colony is present.

In the case of *Cynopterus*, the specialised nature of its roosting habits makes it more difficult to accommodate in the urban sprawl. Potentially suitable roosts are useless unless located within reasonable flying distance of food sources. For *Cynopterus* in Hong Kong this means a variety of plant species fruiting at various times of the year to ensure constant supply. The bats have been seen feeding on the purple berries of *Schefflera octophylla* (family Araliaceae) and bananas (G. Ades, pers. comm., 1991), and the warty figs of the Chinese banyan tree, *Ficus retusa*, (Marshall and Hechtel, 1966). In all probability they also utilise the syconia of some of the other 27 *Ficus* species present in Hong Kong as well (22 species are native).

It seems strange at first to think of wild fruit bats living within five minutes' walk of the fumes and clatter of the daily rush of Hong Kong's Central District. The lifestyle of *Cynopterus* appears almost withdrawn — resting quietly in small groups or in solitude — compared to the robust, rackety agglomerations of *Pteropus*, which seem somehow more in tune with a metropolis. However, in the course of that five-minute walk from Queen's Road, in the deep green shade, as the root-fractured surface of Battery Path snakes up the hillside toward the massive cream wall of the Government House Compound, the traffic noise dulls to a hum. Waiting to cross the road from Government House to the stone splendour of the entrance to the Botanical Gardens, one glances upward to the dark green, jungly slopes of Victoria Peak beyond. In spite of the often capacious dwellings secreted amongst the tucks and folds of green-draped hillsides, it is easy to imagine a wealth of wildlife finding food and shelter there. Perhaps *Cynopterus*'s prospects will be better on the island than in the sterile over-development of the New Territories.

People often find it odd that, as a naturalist, I should claim Hong Kong as one of my favourite places on earth, on a list which includes deserts and jungles rather than cities. Perhaps this is because they have missed the violent and exciting contrast between the concrete 'hornets' nest' of traders and rapacious tourists and the heavy silence of the tangled mountain greenery, or the calm, shimmering expanses of water, disturbed only by the assortment of waders milling about the shallows of the Mai Po marshes. Nearby, at low tide, the mudflats fringed by mangroves glitter with mudskippers in the gentle grey light of early morning — visible as a shimmer in the distance is the human clamour of China.

It is always hard to leave Hong Kong for the 'civilisation', set fast in concrete and bitumen, of Frankfurt and London — in spite of the lure of reunions with zoos, museums and much-missed friends. This was to be a bat hunt of a different kind; pursuing the dusky flying-fox through the cavernous storage chambers of museums, scrabbling through innumerable boxes of bones and drawers filled with age-desiccated skins, the wings stiff and brittle, set in casually unnatural attitudes of death.

The dusky flying-fox, *Pteropus brunneus,* is an irritating animal. I use the singular advisedly because only one specimen of the beast has so far presented itself to science. It has been on and off the list of Australian mammals a number of times, alternatively regarded as an extinct species or a vagrant from elsewhere in the region. When I mentioned to Greg Richards my intention of ferreting through the pteropids of the Senckenberg Museum, Frankfurt, and the Natural History Museum in London, he invited me to join him and Les Hall in an effort to settle the legitimacy of *P. brunneus,* Hall and Richards having reconsidered their relegation of the dusky flying-fox to the status of a 'blow-in' in their publication *Bats of Eastern Australia* (1979).

Upon reflection they had decided that the distance involved in its arrival on Percy Island, near Mackay, Queensland, from the Louisiade Archipelago, off the southeast tip of Papua New Guinea, or any other likely areas was simply too great to be probable. It is possible, however, for a small flying-fox to be transported over considerable stretches by cyclones, and the larger flying-foxes can certainly cover considerable distances in flight. W. T. Blanford, in his *Fauna of British India including Burma and Ceylon* (1888–91), refers to Sterndale having caught a live flying-fox at sea, 200 miles (320 kilometres) from land. Be that as it may, the question remains — even if the *Pteropus brunneus* on Percy Island were a windblown waif, why have none of its conspecifics turned up elsewhere?

Illogical as it seemed, circumstances dictated that I should begin the search in Frankfurt, at the Senckenberg Museum, which houses the second largest chiropteran collection in Europe, presided over by Dr Dieter Kock, a veteran of many years' distinguished bat work, amongst other things mammalogical, and maker of possibly the most abominable coffee I have ever tasted. The days at the

Senckenberg were a delight. Spurred on by the great kindness and generosity of Dr Kock and his assistant Frau Altmann, enthusiasm overcame jetlag and I ploughed through trays full of specimens, measuring and photographing. I was not really expecting to find an undiscovered second specimen of the dusky flying-fox, but hoped to become familiar with the range of variation within the related *P. hypomelanus* group for comparison, amongst other things. I also looked at animals collected within the area from which *P. brunneus* might have come, if it were indeed a waif from elsewhere. I was also attempting to build up a photographic library of the skulls of as many *Pteropus* species as possible to which I could refer in the future.

For someone more accustomed to dealing with live animals, it is something of a shock to the system to spend days on end up to the elbows in assorted bits and pieces of dead ones. I was therefore doubly grateful to be able to at least begin and end my day by observing a large and lively colony of short-tailed fruit bats, *Carollia perspicillata*, (a frugivorous microchiropteran found in the neotropical lowlands from southern Mexico to northern Argentina) in the nocturnal house of Frankfurt Zoo. This was thanks to the good offices of Dr Richard Faust, the director, who had arranged accommodation for me in one of the zoo's guestrooms.

Apart from bat-related matters, this also gave me the opportunity, as in the past, to wander the zoo's gardens and exhibits in those magically tranquil hours of early morning and evening when the general public is excluded — the times when the animals can be observed and drawn in peace. The countless pages of pen drawings produced in such delightfully privileged circumstances have not only formed the basis of many exhibitions of paintings, but also represent for me a wordless diary. Perhaps this is why I am almost invariably reluctant to part with these mostly minimal line sketches, executed in minutes, usually after hours of observation.

People invariably ask how long it takes to do a drawing or painting, to which, particularly in the case of the pen studies, the honest answer is most of my life. These are either works of art or disasters to be relegated to the bin — there is no room to hide or correct a mistake. Like many other artists I know, every time one is successful, it feels more like alchemy than skill and I am pessimistically convinced that I shall never manage to pull it off again. In truth the process is for the most part less mysterious. Drawing is like playing the piano: technically it is a matter of constant exercise — playing one's scales — developing the coordination between hand and eye until it is possible to translate to the paper what the eye sees without having to flick glances between the two. I find drawing in the dark halls of nocturnal houses in zoos excellent practice for this. The rest is a combination of confidence and the inspiration provided by the subject.

After time enough in Frankfurt to establish just how much I still did not know, but roughly in which directions to look, I had to leave for London. After the traditional welcome of roast beef and Yorkshire pud at what has become my alternative home, complete with alternative parents in the shape of Nancy and Ron Ashenden, I sallied forth to the 'wicked' city of London. Ron's warnings about muggings, coshings and suspicious parcels haunted me through the eerie, somehow lavatorial, subway leading from the train to that imposing Victorian edifice, the Natural History Museum. On entering this building I always have the urge to simply lie on my back on the cool tiled floor and take in the majestic spectacle of it all — the staircase, the magnificent ceilings, the atmosphere. It was sad, on a later visit, to see that the dead hand of modernisation — and the assumption that change is progress — had marred the beautiful historic galleries.

Nevertheless, the backbone of a museum is its collections, and it was the vast mammal collection of this one that I had come to see. More to the point, this, the largest collection of Chiroptera in Europe, is the repository of the one and only *Pteropus brunneus*. I could lay hands on the beast at last.

I had already spent many hours in the library of the Museum of Victoria, pursuing the dusky flying-fox through the literature, chasing unlikely leads amongst various journals of the mid- to late 19th century, as well as reading the opinions of modern systematists on its validity as a 'good', that is, distinct, species. Having reached the conclusion that it is on the latter point legitimate, my major concern was the question of whether it could justifiably be included in the checklist of Australian species. In London, I was as much interested in finding out more about the provenance of the specimen as in the bat itself.

Our starting point was the information that the animal had been collected on Percy Island by Captain Mangles Denham of the hydrographic survey vessel HMS *Herald*. The Percy Islands, a group of three, are located off the Queensland coast near Mackay. One of the islands was frequented as a watering stop by the sailing ships plying those waters in the last century. On board many of these ships were naturalists, both amateur and professional, of some competence, and avid collectors of specimens of a fauna still relatively new to them. The HMS *Herald* alone carried not only Captain Denham, but the surgeons Rayner and MacDonald, who were creditable suppliers of scientific material to various museums in the course of their voyages. It is therefore puzzling that no other specimens of *P. brunneus* have turned up in collections from these much-visited islands.

The only confirmation of the species' presence in the putative type locality is the colourful paper by Dr Thomas P. Lucas, MRCSE, (see also chapter 11), entitled *The Flying-fox: Its habits and depredations*. This was read before the Royal Society of Queensland in 1896 and duly published in its proceedings. Unfortunately no references are cited, so we must take Dr Lucas at his word. As the title suggests, the paper is not primarily concerned with *P. brunneus*, but does make some interesting incidental comments on it. In his general description of flying-foxes, the author mentions the presence of glands secreting a substance that gives the animals a characteristic odour and asserts that in *P. brunneus* this scent resembles musk. The question is, how did he know? Had he actually seen and smelt the animal? If not, who had provided this information? A little further on, he reports that a Mr Broadbent, presumably Kendal Broadbent, collector, taxidermist and ornithologist, claims to have seen a camp of this species flying over the coast of the mainland opposite Percy Island, adding that *P. brunneus* is plentiful on the latter.

Interestingly, Lucas shows caution in accepting this as a fifth Australian species, and will accept it as such only if Broadbent is correct. It is not clear whether he accepts as common knowledge that the species is abundant on Percy Island, but leaves room for doubt in Broadbent's identification of the particular group of animals seen flying over the coast, or whether the whole statement is an unconfirmed observation by that gentleman. Broadbent presumably had some experience of flying-foxes, having at least collected them in New Guinea, but identifying a species in flight can be extremely difficult, even for an experienced observer. Both black and spectacled flying-foxes have been collected on Percy Island, although these species are distinctly larger than the dusky flying-fox. Confusion between the latter and the little red flying-fox would seem more likely to occur, on the basis of their size.

However, that is all there seems to be in reference to the dusky flying-fox as far as observation of living animals goes. The other accounts refer to this or to descriptions of the British Museum specimen.

I removed the dry, almost weightless skin, packed out with cotton wool, and the skull, couched separately in a small pale cardboard box, from the type specimens cabinet. Carefully, I carried it to a table beneath one of the small, high windows set into the thick walls, looking out over the roof tops. The bat is — or was — a male adult, certainly not a spectacular animal as flying-foxes go, being rather small — Greg Richards's estimate based on the forearm measurement of 118 millimetres is that it probably weighed around 200 grams when alive, that is, roughly one-quarter of the weight of an adult male grey-headed flying-fox. The fur on the body, now some 160 or so years old, felt crisp yet satin-slippery as I ran my fingers along its darkish, warm brown back. Immediately below the shoulders, the texture changes, with long silky guard hairs lying flat against the body, combining with a shorter, woollier underlayer. The fur extends, although sparsely, along the backs of the lower legs. I felt amongst the lighter, livelier coloured fur of the mantle, with its slight staple different to the rest, eventually locating the two tufts of straw-coloured bristles that marked its scapular glands. Turning it over, the ventral surface differed little in colour from the dorsal, perhaps marginally lighter brown. The wizened face with its vacant cotton wool eyes was a russet-tinged golden brown, lightening over the top of the head near the mantle. Thinking over the published descriptions of the skin, I wondered how much time had faded its original colours and how much individual perceptions of colour differed.

Could it be that this small, un-obtrusively coloured species had simply been overlooked by the collectors of the past, or mistaken for 'just another

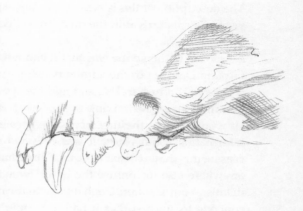

Detail of the skull of the dusky flying-fox (*Pteropus brunneus*).

flying-fox' by people happening on it in the wild? Some species of *Pteropus* pursue a less gregarious lifestyle than those found on the Australian mainland. Perhaps *P. brunneus* was, or for that matter is, one that roosts singly or in pairs, unlikely to be noticed scattered around a remote habitat. Its relatively hefty dental equipment suggests that it is principally a fruit (as opposed to nectar and blossom) eater. Richards and Hall have surmised that the widespread clearing and replanting of the coastline near Mackay with sugar cane might have robbed the species of vital feeding grounds within range of their island roost. I hope one day we shall find out.

Having examined the skin of the bat, I looked more closely at the narrow, yellowing strip of stiffened paper attached to its leg. On this I found the usual information; that is, the name of the collector, Captain Denham; the locality, Percy Island; the age and sex of the animal and a registration number. The number was of particular interest, being a type of museum code. This was explained for me by Daphne Hills of the mammal department: 74.3.16.2 could be translated into date of registration at the museum, 16 March, 1874 and the final digit indicated that it was the second of a group of specimens acquired. On checking the original note of registration in the old book we found that what was now *Pteropus brunneus* had been purchased from Stevens' Sale Room, mistakenly labelled as a black flying-fox. It had been accompanied by one which actually was a Black. This in itself was of no great moment, although it caused me to speculate again on the possibility that others of its kind had simply mouldered away unrecognised in private collections.

The description of this specimen as a new species had not been published until four years after its arrival in the museum collection, in Dobson's monumental work on the Chiroptera.

What bothered me was that it had not arrived, as I had assumed, directly from Captain Denham or the admiralty. Moreover there was a gap of 13 years between the *Herald*'s return to England and the specimen's arrival at the museum. This left plenty of scope for mixing up or losing the original labels, among other things. It would not be the first time. The species identity was no great bother, but the information about where it was collected was. However, it was in a strange way reassuring that at least no other specimen of *P. brunneus* had turned up from anywhere else to confuse the issue. Even if I would have liked some confirming details about Captain Denham's actual capture of the animal, there was nothing concrete to suggest that it had not come from one of the Percy isles. Stalemate. Along the lines of the principle innocent until proved guilty, I think it reasonable to presume this species Australian until proved otherwise. If so, it is probably another sad case of an animal lost before we had time to know it. Fortunately fate may be kinder, or at least better managed, for some other species of *Pteropus* in danger of sharing the fate of *P. brunneus*.

After a week of sifting through dead bats in the Natural History Museum and looking at live ones in London Zoo, I landed in Jersey eagerly anticipating several days in one of my favourite zoos. The headquarters of the Jersey Wildlife Preservation Trust is in fact far more than a zoo, it is a centre for the breeding of endangered species and the development of conservation programmes in their countries of origin, a provider of training for conservation biologists from all over the world, a negotiator with governments on behalf of threatened wildlife, and more. This is no mere collection of exotic furred and feathered stamps, as many zoos have been in the past (and some still are).

As usual, the chronic jetlag by this stage glazing my faculties was dispelled by the air of enthusiasm pervading the place — particularly anywhere within earshot of Trust Secretary Simon Hicks, whose energy is at once inspiring and appalling! I arrived with the intention of finding out the latest about the trust's work with the Rodrigues flying-fox and to spend some time observing the breeding colony's behaviour for comparative purposes. Simon, however, had even more exciting news on the pteropid front. The Trust's SAFE (Saving Animals From Extinction) programme now included not just the little golden flying-foxes of Rodrigues, but a Fruit Bats of the Indian Ocean project. They were taking on that magnificent 'chiropteran yeti' the Livingstone's fruit bat (*P. livingstonii*). At that stage little more was known about these huge black, teddy bear-eared bats, than that they were down to something like 150 to 200 individuals in the wild, and

The dog-faced fruit bat (*Cynopterus sphinx sphinx*) in Hong Kong.

The so-called flying lemur or *Colugo* and the dog-faced fruit bat.

the small amount that could be gleaned from the specimens sent to the Natural History Museum in London by Livingstone when he visited the Comores in the course of his Zambesi expedition.

Judging by the Trust's success in breeding and studying the Rodrigues flying-foxes, there was every reason for optimism, if a founder group of *P. livingstonii* could be captured and brought to Jersey.

The survival of the Rodrigues flying-fox in its 110 square kilometre volcanic island home has been jeopardised by a number of factors, including habitat destruction and being killed directly by either humans or the cylones that periodically devastate what little the human population has left of the island's forests. Also, many of the bats starve to death as a consequence of the latter. Such problems are not uncommon threats to small, vulnerable island populations of *Pteropus*. By 1975, the numbers of *P. rodricensis* on Rodrigues were estimated at somewhere between 60 and 80 animals. Since then there have been expansions and crashes in population numbers. However, with a combination of protective legislation, local education and a successful captive breeding programme, there is hope for the future of this species.

In 1976, in cooperation with the Mauritian Government, Gerald Durrell, Founder and Honorary Director of the Jersey Wildlife Preservation Trust, led an expedition to Rodrigues, which he describes in his excellent book, *Golden Bats and Pink Pigeons* (Collins, 1977). Of the 29 bats captured, six males and 13 females went to Black River, Mauritius, and three males and seven females to Jersey, to form the nucleus of the captive breeding programme. The first births at the Trust took place five months after the bats' arrival. The breeding rate was sufficiently successful for the group to be divided in 1982, allowing another separate colony to be established at the Trust and also one at Chester Zoo in England. When dealing with rare species it is a comforting thought to have one's eggs in a spare basket or two in case of mishaps in the form of disease or other disasters. Later colonies were also established at a number of other zoos. By early 1991 the Jersey Zoo Taxon report indicated that there were currently 85 *P. rodricensis* divided between the reverse day/night bat house and the supplementary colony outside, 77 of which were captive-born animals.

Over the years I had been avidly reading the reports in the *Dodo*, the journal of the Jersey Wildlife Preservation Trust, of various studies carried out by people associated with the Trust into the behaviour and social structures of *P. rodricensis*. I looked forward to discussing this with Dr Bryan Carroll, the Curator of Mammals and with the bat staff. More than anything though, I wanted to get back to bat watching, after all the necro-zoology of the past weeks. Watching the colony in the bat house, the first thing that struck me was the frequency and apparent

The Rodrigues flying-fox (*Pteropus rodricensis*).

nonchalance with which the animals fluttered to the ground, crawling and flopping about after scraps of food, then taking off again, with far less effort than I had expected. This sort of thing is not generally seen in the much larger *P. poliocephalus* I was used to, except under duress. Bats on the ground are extremely vulnerable to predators. However, for a species to survive on an island prone to cyclones, it is at times necessary to forage at ground level, when trees have been denuded of fruits, flowers and foliage by stripping winds.

The bat staff, led by Janette Young, were kind enough to not only answer a plethora of questions, but also to let me participate in the morning feed at the bat house. There are about 44 flying-foxes in this reverse daylight house, and food is distributed over ten feeding sites located against the walls or suspended from perches. This allows less dominant animals an opportunity to get their share of the mixture of chopped apples, oranges, bananas, cabbage and carrots, supplemented with whatever is seasonally available in the way of grapes, pears, pineapples, melons and tomatoes. To this is added a mixture also used for marmosets, consisting of prepared New World Primate Pellets soaked in water, with brown bread, golden syrup and high-protein baby cereal. The meal is crowned with a dusting of skim milk powder.

As we entered the twilight of the bats' room from a small side kitchen, a soft rush of air passed my ear with a loose flapping sound; I felt a light touch on my shoulder and looked down. Clinging to my jacket was a diminutive golden brown flying-fox with a round, fuzzy face and short, pointed snout. This, I was told, was Juliet, a tame young bat. I offered her a morsel of banana, which was accepted readily, and waited for an earring to be pulled off, or my plait dragged apart. To my astonishment, Juliet simply sat there, always ready to accept another tidbit, but otherwise unconcerned by all the things that the grey-headed and black flying-foxes of my acquaintance find an irresistible strain on their curiosity.

I stood still, waiting for Juliet to decide to rejoin the others and watched the lively colony go to work on the dishes of food. I had noticed earlier that as far as some of the dominant males are concerned, there is no such thing as a free lunch: as they grabbed and copulated with females visiting their feeding territories. Quietly I speculated on the possibility of the Rodrigues bats' breeding success being emulated with *P. livingstonii*. The thought was tremendously exciting.

Livingstone's fruit bat was first described as a species by Gray and published in the *Proceedings of the Zoological Society* in 1866, three years after the first specimens were shot by Dr Livingstone on what was then known as Johanna Island. At the time they were regarded as common in the Comores, a volcanic archipelago in the Mozambique Channel near Madagascar. In the modern-day Federal Islamic Republic of the Comores, the forests are disappearing at an alarming rate, overwhelmed by the pressures of human population density and poverty. Trees are consumed as firewood and building material and land is cleared for subsistence crops of bananas, manioc and coconuts. The more fertile pockets of the lower mountain slopes are taken up with crops of vanilla and ylang ylang, destined for export. The great black fruit bats cannot compete with this. They are now restricted to the remnants of primary forest on the steep slopes of the island of Anjouan.

After a particularly devastating cyclone hit the island in 1989, the number of bats dropped to less than one hundred. At this point John Hartley, assistant to Gerald Durrell, began negotiations with the Comores Government, obtaining official blessing for the collection of some of the remaining bats for a captive breeding programme. The first attempt at implementing this, in 1990, failed, however, Bryan Caroll was able to estimate that between 60 and 120 of the bats were present at the roost he visited. Their habit of using the very topmost branches of the high forest canopy made capture difficult. It was not until the following year that the problem of setting nets efficiently at suitable heights was solved by Rob Saw, a member of the Trust who also happened to be a tree surgeon and lecturer in horticulture.

In 1992 Janette Young, Rob Saw and a Bristol University expedition led by Stephanie Wray (studying the bats' feeding ecology and general behaviour) were at last successful. Five males and one female became the inaugural members of the Livingstone's fruit bat breeding programme. In 1993 they were joined by another five males and one more female. The estimation of the population in the wild was no more than 150 and on the way down. Fortunately events in the captive group bode well: not only were two babies born in August and September 1993, but both were females. A suitable display of gratitude perhaps for their expensive diet of mango, avocado, banana and pawpaw!

Efforts are being made to raise funding for further expeditions to establish a more viable founder group of ten females to ten males, and carry out research on the wild population. I am anxiously awaiting the chance to return to Jersey and meet these spectacular animals, with their 1.5-metre wingspans, among the largest members of *Pteropus*, a genus filled with fascinating beasts.

Epilogue

When asked to give a talk on bats some time ago, I began casting around for a theme to use as the framework for the lecture. This led me to the idea of drawing up a sort of scoreboard . . . what bats do for humans, measured against what humans do for bats — an exchange of benefits. The result was that, directly and indirectly, bats do rather more for us than we appear to be doing for them. Narrowing it down to the flying-foxes, the conclusion was much the same.

The majority of *Pteropus* species have a small, and thus vulnerable, distribution. Fifty-five of the 65 or so species are island dwellers and of these, 35 are restricted either to single islands or to small island groups. Thirty-eight species range through areas of at most 50 square kilometres, another 22 are restricted to land areas of less than 10 square kilometres. (Rainey and Pierson, 1992.) Bearing this in mind, let us look at what they are up against.

Flying-foxes and forests (in some cases mangroves) are inextricably bound in terms of survival (we have already looked at this in earlier chapters). In the past, the island dwellers have coped well with the pressures placed on them by nature, recovering in due course from the ravages of typhoons, volcanic activity and the like. On many islands natural predators were not a problem for flying-foxes. However, as with so many other species, the overwhelming increase in human population has created an impossible competition for resources, as well as increasingly heavy pressure from hunting and the introduction of predators.

In the last 20 years or so we have seen a decline in populations of many island species of *Pteropus,* corresponding to a dramatic reduction of the forests and mangroves due to logging and the increased demand for space for crops and development. Regrettably, human and *Pteropus* populations tend to exploit similar areas on most islands. Inevitably the flying-foxes lose out. With a relatively slow rate of reproduction and the disappearance of alternative feeding and roosting areas to which they can resort after destructive typhoons or cyclones, they are seriously disadvantaged in terms of maintaining a viable population, even without direct pressure from hunting. Habitat is the key to survival. Without the forests, flying-foxes lack food, roosting and breeding areas, they are left vulnerable to human hunters and predators, and populations become fragmented, restricted to remnant pockets of habitat and more vulnerable to extinction.

Although many excellent people are working hard at the task of researching the biology of flying-foxes, we still know far too little to manage most species effectively for their ultimate survival. In some cases, there is very little time left to find out more and if conservation measures are not taken swiftly, they will join the ranks of species lost to us before we know much more of them than a case of dust-dry skins in the drawer of a museum.

At the Healesville Sanctuary, the grey-headed flying-fox group has grown, although some of the original members have left. BRW2, that successful sire dominating the far quadrants, has been removed, along with some of the young males. BRW2 was becoming rather too successful in terms of genetic representation in the group. The predominance of male offspring, with the exception of Leonora, in the last few years meant that the sex ratio of the group needed rebalancing, hence the weeding out of a few who have been transferred elsewhere.

BRWF, mother of Richard, now seems to have the hang of procreation, however late she came to it. She has continued to produce a youngster annually, though never again with the drama of Richard's arrival.

Old 010, Roger's mother, looks smaller and greyer than ever. She lost one infant after her golden son, Phil, probably as a consequence of her age and harsh weather compromising her condition for some time after the birth. It was touching to watch her in the first season of Roger's adulthood, coming to him on chilly days and roosting huddled against him for warmth — something I never saw him object to or avoid.

010B, the serene and tolerant mother of Lucy, Flash and co., has continued to produce her annual offspring. Her son, SM, whom we first met returning as a one-year-old to his mother's breast before the birth of Lucy, has become a successful inseminator, dominating Scruff's old territory and females.

Endora now lives with Witch, behind the scenes in the Sanctuary's education facility, doing a first-rate job of pteropid public relations with the many children who come to meet her. She remains as tame and full of curiosity as ever. I still visit her there from time to time, sharing a favourite game in which Endora, who has a passion for hair, woolly jumpers and jewellery, grasps the end of my waist-long plait in her teeth and proceeds to climb the wire wall in an attempt to tow me up to the roof. As I later wash the bat-spit from my hair, I am invariably struck by the thought of what an extraordinary privilege it is to share the lives of these complex and intelligent animals. It behoves us to ensure that future generations will also have the opportunity to do so.

Healesville
2nd March, 1994.

Appendices

GENEALOGIES

Scruff?	Sm	Sm?	Split?	BRW2	BRW2	Roger?
+	+	+	+	+	+	+
010	010	Spot	Spot	010B	BRWF	Fang
Roger	Phil	DNS*	PMale	Sm?	Richard	001#
			Fang	Lucy	Whatsit	
				Flash	001	
				Kee		
				001		

NON-BREEDERS

Male BRW1   Male LBW   Endora

* Did not survive.
#Taken over by Spot.

MAP OF STUDY AREA AND TERRITORIES

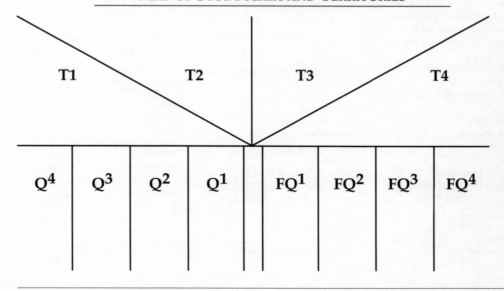

T1   T2   T3   T4

Q^4 Q^3 Q^2 Q^1 FQ^1 FQ^2 FQ^3 FQ^4

APPENDIX II

SOME WILD FOOD SPECIES UTILISED BY AUSTRALIAN *PTEROPUS*

Myrtaceae
Eucalyptus maculata, Spotted Gum[+]
E. beyeri, Beyer's Ironbark
E. gummifera, Red Bloodwood
E. grandis, Flooded Gum[+]
E. robusta, Swamp Mahogany
E. citriodora, Lemon-scented Gum
E. cloeziana
E. intermedia, Pink Bloodwood
E. polycarpa
E. tereticornis, Forest Red Gum[+]
E. albens
E. confertiflora
E. camaldulensis, River Gum[+]
E. porrecta
E. pilularis, Blackbutt[+]
E. saligna, Bluegum[+]
E. moluccana, Grey Box
E. paniculata, Grey Ironbark[+]
E. fibrosa, Broad-leaved Ironbark
E. eximia, Yellow Bloodwood
E. propinqua, Small-fruited Grey Gum
E. punctata, Large-fruited Grey Gum[+]
E. parramattensis, Parramatta,
  Calgaroo, Drooping or Dirty Red
  Gum[+]
Syncarpia glomulifera, Turpentine
Lophostemon confertus, Brush Box
Melaleuca quinquenervia, Broad-leafed
  Tea Tree
Angophora costata, Smooth-barked
  Apple
Angophora floribunda, Rough-barked
  Apple[+]
Syzigium forte
S. dictyophlebium
S. kuranda
S. wesa
S. australe, Brush Cherry
S. oleosum, Blue Lilly Pilly
Acmena smithii, Lilly Pilly
Eugenia sp.?
Decaspermum humile
Burseraceae
Canarium muelleri

Leguminoseae
Castanospermum australe
Elaeocarpaceae
E. angustifolius
E. bancroftii
E. obovatus, Hard Quandong
Sapotaceae
Manilkara kauki
Planchonella australis, Black Apple
Rosaceae
*Parinari nonda**
Annonaceae
Polyalthia micheali
Combretaceae
Terminalia arenicola
T. catappa
T. sericocarpa
Moraceae
Ficus macrophylla
F. crassipes
F. fraseri, Sandpaper Fig
F. pleurocarpa
*F. triradiata**
F. virens var. *sublanceolata*
F. watkinsiana
F. rubiginosa, Port Jackson Fig
F. coronata, Sandpaper Fig
F. obliqua, Small-leaved Fig
Maclura cochinchinensis, Cockspur
  Thorn
Meliaceae
Melia azedarach var. *australasica*
Rutaceae
Achronychia acidula
Verbenaceae
*Faradaya splendida**
Rubiaceae
Nauclea orientalis
Arecaceae
Archontophoenix alexandrae
A. cunninghamiana, Bangalow Palm
Livistona australis, Cabbage Palm
Lauraceae
Neolitsea dealbata
Proteacae
Grevillea robusta, Silky Oak

Banksia integrifolia, Coast Banksia
Banksia serrata, Old Man Banksia
Solanaceae
Solanum mauritanian
Rhamnaceae
Alphitonia excelsa, Red Ash
Vitaceae
Cissus hypoglauca, Water Vine
Sapindaceae
Diploglottis australis, Native Tamarind
Euphorbiaceae
Mallotus discolor, White Kamala
Ehretiaceae
Ehretia acuminata, Koda
Monimiaceae
Hedycarya angustifolia, Native
  Mulberry
Urticaceae
Dendrocnide excelsa, Stinging tree
Loranthaceae
Notothixos cornifolius, Kurrajong
  Mistletoe

(Parry-Jones, 1986, 1991, Richards
  1986 & 1990, Eby 1991, McCoy
  1989) Kuringai Bat Committee
  Inc. Australasian Bat Society
  Newsletter 1, 1993.)
* Richards 1990 fed in captivity.
+ Reported to be browsed by koalas.

CULTIVATED FRUITS UTILISED

Mango	Cashew
Pawpaw	Lychee
Guava	Tamarind
Custard Apple	Soursop
Rollinia	Banana
Orange	Mandarin
Peach	Nectarin
Persimmon	Longan
Carambola	Queen Palm

(Richards 1990 & Loebel, R. 1986)

A P P E N D I X   I I I

SOCIETIES CONCERNED WITH THE STUDY AND CONSERVATION OF BATS

Australasian Bat Society
P.O. Box 612
Milsons Point NSW 2061

Bat Conservation International, Inc.
P.O. Box 162603
Austin
Texas 78716
USA

Bat Groups of Britain
C/o Vincent Wildlife Trust and
Mammal Society
Andrew Weir & Co. Ltd
Dexter House
2 Royal Mint Court
London EC3N 4XX

Jersey Wildlife Preservation Trust
SAFE
Fruit Bats of the Indian Ocean Project
Trinity
Jersey
English Channel Islands

ONARR (Orphaned Native Animal
Rear and Release Programme —
Bat Register)
P.O. Box 15
Darra Qld 4076

**Wildlife Preservation Society
of Queensland**
Brisbane West Branch
8 Clifton Street
Petrie Terrace
Brisbane Qld 4000

Ku-ring-gai Bat Colony Committee
45 Highfield Road
Lindfield NSW 2070

WIRES (Wildlife & Information
 Rescue Service)
Forestville Public School
Melwood Avenue
Forestville NSW 2087

**The Wildlife Animal Rescue and
Care Society, Inc. (ARC)**
RMB 30 Wambina Road
Matcham, NSW 2250
Wambina Flying-fox Research Centre
Wambina Road
Matcham NSW 2250

Batwatch
Royal Zoological Society
P.O. Box 20
Mosman NSW 2088

Bibliography

Abdulali, H., 1948, 'Bat migration in India and other notes on bats'; *J. Bombay Nat. Hist. Soc.*, 47: 522–526.

Ades, G., *Bats of Hong Kong*, World Wildlife Fund.

Aflalo, F.G., 1896. A Sketch of the Natural History of Australia with Some Notes on Sport; McMillan & Co. Ltd, London.

Allen, G.M., 1939, *Bats*; Harvard University Press, Cambridge, Massachusetts.

Alston, E.R., 1874, 'On a new species of *Pteropus* from Samoa'; *Proc. Zool. Soc. Lond.*

Andersen, K., 1908, 'Twenty new forms of *Pteropus*'; *Ann. Mag. Nat. Hist.*, (8) 2: 361–370.

Anderson, K., 1912, *Catalogue of the Chiroptera in the collection of the British Museum, 1. Megachiroptera*, 2nd. edn.; British Museum (Natural History), London.

Archbold, R. and Rand, A.L., *New Guinea Expedition Fly River Area*, 1936–1937; Robert M. McBride & Company, New York.

Augee, M.L., 1990, 'Eighth international bat research conference report to council'; *Australian Zoologist*, vol. 26 (3 & 4).

Baker, J.R. and Baker, Z., 1936, 'The seasons in a tropical rainforest (New Hebrides), pt. 3, fruit bats (Pteropidae)'; *J. Linn. Soc. (Zool.)*, 40: 123–142.

Baker, R.J., Novacek, M.J. & Simmons, N.B., 1991, 'On the monophyly of bats'; *Systematic Zoology*, vol. 40, 2: 216–231.

Bani, E., 1992, 'Fruit bats of Vanuatu'; *Pacific Island Flying-foxes: Proceedings of an International Conservation Conference*, Eds Wilson, D.E. and Graham, G.L.; Biological Report 90(23).

Bartholomew, G.A., Leitner, P. and Nelson, J.E., 1964, 'Body temperature, oxygen consumption, and heart rate in 3 species of Australian flying-foxes'; *Physiological Zoology*, vol. XXXVII, no. 2; University of Chicago.

Blandford, W.T., 1888–91, 'The fauna of British India including Ceylon and Burma'; *Mammalia*, Taylor & Francis, London.

Bock, W.J., 1992, 'The species concept in theory and practice'; *Zoological Science*, 9: 697–712.

Brautigam, A. and Elmquist, T., 1990, 'Conserving Pacific Island flying-foxes'; *Oryx*, vol. 24, no. 2.

Brautigam, A., 1992, 'Conservation of Pacific Island flying-foxes and the convention on international trade in endangered species of wild fauna and flora'; *Pacific Island Flying-foxes: Proceedings of an International Conservation Conference*, Eds Wilson, D.E. and Graham, G.L.; Biological Report 90(23).

Breadon, G., 1931, 'Local migration of the flying-fox (*Pteropus giganteus*) in the Punjab'; *J. Bombay Nat. Hist. Soc.*, 35: 439.

Calford, M.B. and McAnally, K.I., 1987, 'Hearing in flying-foxes (Chiroptera: Pteropodidae)'; *Aust. Mammal*, vol. 10, no. 2.

Carroll, J.B., 1979, 'The general behavioural repertoire of the Rodrigues fruit bat in captivity'; *The Dodo*, Jersey Wildlife Preservation Trust, no. 16.

Carroll, B., 1990, 'Rarest bat gets rarer'; *On the Edge*, no. 61, Jersey Wildlife Preservation Trust.

Champion, I.F., 1932, *Across New Guinea from the Fly to the Sepik*; Constable & Co. Ltd, London.

Cheke, A.S. and Dahl, J.F., 1981, 'The status of bats on western Indian Ocean islands, with special reference to *Pteropus*'; *Mammalia*, 45: 205–238.

Collett, R., 1897, 'On a collection of mammals from north and northwest Australia'; *Proc. Zool. Soc. Lond.*, 317–336.

Conder, P., 1990, 'Flying-foxes or fruit bats?'; *Zoo News*, vol.10: 1.

Cox, P.A., 1983, 'Observations on the natural history of Samoan bats'; *Mammalia*, 47: 519–523.

Cox, P.A., Elmquist, T., Pierson, E., and Rainey, W.E., 1992, 'Flying-foxes as pollinators and seed dispersers in Pacific Island ecosystems'; *Pacific Island Flying-foxes: Proceedings of an International Conservation Conference*, Eds Wilson, D.E. and Graham, G.L.; Biological Report 90(23).

Craig, P. and Syron, W., 1992, 'Fruit bats in American Samoa: their status and future'; *Pacific Island Flying-foxes: Proceedings of an International Conservation Conference*, Eds Wilson, D.E. and Graham, G.L.; Biological Report 90(23).

Cuvier, The Baron, MDCCCXXVII, *The Animal Kingdom arranged in conformity with its organisation, with additional descriptions of all the species hitherto named, and of many not before noticed, by Edward Griffith, F.L.S., A.S. &c. and others*, vol. II; Geo. B. Whittaker, London.

Dallas, W.S., MDCCCLVI, *A Natural History of the*

Animal Kingdom; being a Systematic and Popular Description of the habits, structure and classification of animals from the lowest to the highest forms; Houlston & Stoneman; W.S. Orr & Co., London.

Dee, W.G. and Ballesfin, A.R., 1992, 'Fruit bat population and conservation status in the Philippines'; *Pacific Island Flying-foxes: Proceedings of an International Conservation Conference,* Eds Wilson D.E. and Graham, G.L.; Biological Report 90(23).

Dobson, G.E., 1877a, 'On a collection of Chiroptera from Duke of York Island and the adjacent parts of New Ireland and New Britain'; *Proc. Zool. Soc. Lond.,* 114–127.

Dobson, G.E., 1878, 'Notes on recent additions to the collection of Chiroptera in the Museum d'Histoire Naturelle at Paris, with descriptions of new and rare species'; *Proc. Zool. Soc. Lond.*

Durrell, G., 1977, *Golden Bats and Pink Pigeons,* Collins.

Eby, P., 1991, 'Seasonal movements of grey-headed flying-foxes, *Pteropus poliocephalus* (Chiroptera: Pteropodidae), from two maternity camps in northern New South Wales'; *Wildl. Res.,* 18: 547–559.

Eby, P., 1991, 'Finger-winged night workers: managing forests to conserve the role of grey-headed flying-foxes as pollinators and seed dispersers'; *Conservation of Australia's Forest Fauna,* Ed. Daniel Lunney; Royal Zoological Society of NSW, Mosman.

Falanruw, M.V.C., 1988, 'On the status, reproductive biology and management of fruit bats of Yap'; *Micronesica,* 21 (1–2), 39–51.

Falanruw, M.C. and Manmaw, C.J., 1992, 'Protection of flying-foxes on Yap Islands; *Pacific Island Flying-foxes: Proceedings of an International Conservation Conference,* Eds Wilson, D.E. and Graham, G.L.; Biological Report 90(23).

Felten, H. and Kock, D., 1972, Weitere Flughunde der Gattung *Pteropus* von den Neuen Hebriden sowie den Banks u. Torres Strait Inseln — Pazifischer Ozean; Senckenberg Biol. 45: 179–188.

Fenton, M. Brock, 1983, *Just Bats;* University of Toronto Press, Toronto, Buffalo, London.

Flannery, T., 1992, 'Bats, rats and BHP: "Rare" species and mining in remote areas'; *BHP Review,* vol. 70, no. 5

Flannery, T. and Seri, L., 1993, 'The fall and rise of Bulmer's fruit bat'; *Australian Natural History,* vol. 24: 7.

Flower, S.S., 1900, 'The mammals of Siam and the Malay Peninsula'; *Proc. Zool. Soc. Lond.*

Forbes, H.O., 1885, *A Naturalist's Wanderings in the Eastern Archipelago: a Narrative of Travel and Exploration from 1878 to 1883;* Sampson Low, Marston, Searle & Rivington, London.

Goodman, B., 'Holy phylogeny! Did bats evolve twice?'; *Science,* vol. 253.

Goodwin, R.E., 1979, 'The bats of Timor: systematics and ecology'; *Bulletin of the American Museum of Natural History,* 163: 73–122.

Gould, J., 1849, 'On new species of mammalia and birds from Australia'; *Proc. Zool. Soc. Lond.* 1849, 109–110.

Graham, G.L., 1992, 'Conservation and subsistence harvesting of Pacific Island flying-foxes'; *Pacific Island Flying-foxes: Proceedings of an International Conservation Conference,* Eds Wilson, D.E. and Graham G.L.; Biological Report 90(23).

Gray, J.E., 1870, *Catalogue of Monkeys, Lemurs and Fruit-eating Bats in the British Museum.*

Gray, J.E., 1858, 'List of species of mammalia sent from the Aru Islands by Mr. A.R. Wallace to the British Museum'; *Proc. Zool. Soc. Lond.*

Gray, J.E., 1866a, 'A revision of Pteropine bats (Pteropodidae), and the descriptions of some apparently undescribed species'; *Proc. Zool. Soc. Lond.*

Gray, J.E., 1866b, 'Notes on some mammalia from Port Albany (Cape York Peninsula), north Australia, with the descriptions of some new species'; *Proc. Zool. Soc. Lond.*

Graydon, M., Giorgi, P. and Pettigrew, J., 1987, 'Vision in flying-foxes (Chiroptera: Pteropodidae)'; *Aust. Mammal,* vol. 10, no. 2.

Gunther, A., 1874, 'A contribution to the fauna of Savage Island'; *Proc. Zool. Soc. Lond.*

Gunther, A., 1879, 'List of the mammals, reptiles, and batrachians sent by Mr. Everett from the Philippine Islands'; *Proc. Zool. Soc. Lond.*

Hall, L.S. and Richards, G.C., 1979, *Bats of Eastern Australia;* Queensland Museum Booklet no. 12.

Hall, L. S., 1987, 'Identification, distribution and taxonomy of Australian flying-foxes (Chiroptera: Pteropodidae)'; *Aust. Mammal* vol. 10, no. 2.

Hall, L.S. and Richards, G.C., 1987, 'Crop protection and management of flying-foxes (Chiroptera: Pteropodidae)' *Aust. Mammal,* vol. 10, no. 2.

Hall, L.S. and Richards, G.C., 1991, 'Flying-fox camps'; *Wildlife Australia,* vol. 28, no. 1.

Hamilton-Smith, E., 1980, 'The status of Australian Chiroptera'; *Proc. Fifth International Bat Research Conference,* Eds Wilson, D.E. and Gardner, A.L.; Texas Tech. Press, Lubbock.

Harrison, J., 1966, *An Introduction to Mammals of Singapore and Malaya*, Singapore Branch, Malayan Nature Society.

Hill, J.E., 1971, 'Bats from the Solomon Islands'; *Journal of Natural History*, vol. 5, 573–581.

Hill, J.E. and Smith J.D., 1984, *Bats: A Natural History*; British Museum (Natural History), London.

Hill, J. E. and Thonglongya, K., 1972, 'Bats from Thailand and Cambodia'; *Bull. Brit. Mus. (Nat. Hist.) Zool.*, vol. 22, no. 6, 171–196.

Hyndman, D. and Menzies, J.I., 1980, '*Aproteles bulmerae* (Chiroptera: Pteropodidae) of New Guinea is not extinct'; *J. Mamm.*, 61 (1):159–160.

Ingle, N.R and Heaney, L.R., 1992, 'A key to the bats of the Philippine Islands'; *Fieldiana. Zoology*, new series, no. 69; Field Museum of Natural History.

Iredale, T. and Troughton, E. Le G., 1934, 'A check list of the mammals recorded from Australia'; The Australian Museum Sydney, Memoir VI.

Jentinck, F.A., 1883, 'A list of species of mammals from West Sumatra and North Celebes, with descriptions of undescribed or rare species'; *Notes from the Leyden Museum*, vol. V, 170–181.

Jentinck, F.A., 1906, 'On the New Guinea mammals'; *Notes from the Leyden Museum*, vol. XXVIII, 161–178.

Jepsen, G.L., 1970, 'Bat origins and evolution', In Wimsatt, W.A., Ed.; *Biology of Bats*, vol. 1; Academic Press, New York and London.

Kendell, J., 1991, 'New hope for Western Samoa'; *Habitat Australia*, December.

Kitchener, D.J., Gunnell, A. and Mahradatunkamsi, 1990, 'Aspects of the feeding biology of fruit bats (Pteropodidae) on Lombok Island, Nusa Tenggara, Indonesia'; *Mammalia* 54 (4): 561–578.

Koopman, K.F., 1979, 'Zoogeography of mammals from islands off the northeastern coast of New Guinea'; *American Museum Novitates*, no. 2690; American Museum of Natural History.

Koopman, K.F., 1984, 'Taxonomic and distributional notes on tropical Australian bats'; *American Museum Novitates* 2778, 1–48.

Koopman, K.F. and Gordon, L.K., 1992, 'Systematic notes on a collection of bats from Halmahera (Indonesia: Moluccas)'; *American Museum Novitates*, no. 3035.

Kosaka, E., 1992, 'Making the conservation laws work'; *Pacific Island Flying-foxes: Proceedings of an International Conservation Conference*, Eds Wilson D.E. and Graham, G.L.; Biological Report 90(23).

Kula, G.R., 1992, 'Current status and distribution of fruit bats (Genus *Pteropus*) in Papua New Guinea'; *Pacific Island Flying-foxes: Proceedings of an International Conservation Conference*, Eds Wilson, D.E. and Graham, G.L.; Biological Report 90(23).

Kunz, T.H., Ed., 1982, *Ecology of bats*; Plenum Press, New York and London.

Kuroda, N., 1933, 'A revision of the genus *Pteropus* found in the island of the Riu Kiu Chain, Japan'; *Pteropus* dasymallus wird in 4 Unterarten aufgeteilt, darunter 2 neue; *Jl. of Mammal.*, 14.4: 312–316.

Leche, W., 1884, 'On some species of Chiroptera from Australia'; *Proc. Zool. Soc. London*, 49–54.

Lemke, T.O., 1992, 'Status of the Marianas fruit bat (*Pteropus mariannus*) in the Northern Mariana Islands North of Saipan'; *Pacific Island Flying-foxes: Proceedings of an International Conservation Conference*, Eds Wilson D.E. and Graham, G.L.; Biological Report 90(23).

Lemke, T.O., 1992, 'History of fruit bat use, research, and protection in the Northern Marianna Islands'; *Pacific Island Flying-foxes: Proceedings of an International Conservation Conference*, Eds Wilson, D.E. and Graham, G.L.; Biological Report 90(23).

Le Souef, A.S., Burrell, H., 'The wild animals of Australasia embracing the mammals of New Guinea and the nearer Pacific Islands. With a chapter on the bats of Australia and New Guinea by Ellis Le G. Troughton'; George G. Harrap & Company Ltd, London, Calcutta, Sydney.

Lucas, A.H.S. and Le Souef, 1909, *The Animals of Australia: Mammals, Reptiles and Amphibians*; Whitcombe & Tombs Ltd.

Lucas, T.P., 1896, 'The flying-fox: its habits and depredations'; *Proc. Royal. Soc. Qld.*, vol. XII.

Luckoff, H., 1987, 'Rearing orphan *Pteropus* spp. (Chiroptera: Pteropodidae) for release to the wild'; *Aust. Mammal.*, vol. 10, no. 2.

Lujan, R.J., 1992, 'Local policies and protection by the government of Guam'; *Pacific Island Flying-foxes: Proceedings of an International Conservation Conference*, Eds Wilson, D.E. and Graham, G.L.; Biological Report 90(23).

Lunney, D., 1989; 'Priorities for bat conservation'; *Australian Zoologist*, vol. 25(3).

McCann, C., 1941, 'Further observations on the flying-fox (*Pteropus giganteus* Brunn) and the fulvous fruit-bat (*Rousettus leschenaulti* Desm.)'; *J. Bombay Nat. Hist. Soc.*, 72, 587–592.

McGuckin, M.A. and Blackshaw, A.W., 1987, Cycle

of the seminifierous epithelium in the grey-headed fruit bat, *Pteropus poliocephalus. Aust. J. Biol. Sci.*, 40, 203–210.

McGuckin, M.A. and Blackshaw, A.W., 1987, 'Seasonal changes in spermatogenesis (including germ cell degeneration) and plasma testosterone concentration in the grey-headed fruit bat, *Pteropus poliocephalus*'; *Aust. J. Biol. Sci.*, 40: 211–220.

McKean, J.L. and Simpson, K.G, 1967, 'A Victorian specimen of the little red flying-fox *Pteropus scapulatus*'; *Victorian Naturalist*, 84: 180–81.

McKean, J.L., 1972a, 'Notes on some collections of bats (order Chiroptera) from Papua New Guinea and Bougainville Island'; *CSIRO Div. Wildlife Research. Tech. Paper*, no. 26, 1–35.

McMullen, D.L., 1992, 'United States conservation laws that apply to Pacific Island flying-foxes'; *Pacific Island Flying-foxes: Proceedings of an International Conservation Conference*, Eds Wilson, D.E. and Graham, G.L.; Biological Report 90(23).

McQueen, R.H.J., 1965, 'Fruit bats'; *Victorian Naturalist*, 82: 47–8.

Mahoney, J.A. and Walton, D.W., *Pteropodidae. Zoological Catalogue of Australia, vol. 5; Mammalia;* Bureau of Flora and Fauna, Canberra; Australian Govt. Publishing Service, Canberra.

Marshall, A.J., 1947, 'Breeding cycle of an equatorial bat (*Pteropus giganteus* of Ceylon)'; *Proc. Linn. Soc. Lond.*, 159: 103–111.

Marshall, A.G., 1983, 'Bats, flowers and fruit: evolutionary relationships in the Old World'; *Biological Journal of the Linnean Society*, 20: 115–135.

Marshall, P.M., 1966, 'Notes on fruit bats, *Cynopterus sphinx sphinx* (Vahl), in Hong Kong'; *Memoirs of the Hong Kong Natural History Society*, no. 7.

Martin, L., Towers, P.A., McGuckin, M.A., Little, L., Luckhoff, H. and Blackshaw, A.W, 1987, 'Reproductive biology of flying-foxes (Chiroptera: Pteropodidae)'; *Australian Mammalogy*, vol. 10, no. 2.

Menkhorst, P.W. and Dixon, J.M., 1985, 'Influxes of the grey-headed flying-fox, *Pteropus poliocephalus* (Chiroptera, Pteropodidae), to Victoria in 1981 and 1982'; *Aust. Mammal.*, 8: 117–121.

Menzies, J.I., 1977, 'Fossil and subfossil fruit bats from the mountains of New Guinea'; *Aust. J. Zool.*, 25: 329–336.

Mertens, R., 1930, Bemerkungen uber die Saugetiere der Inseln Lombok, Sumbawa und Flores; Der Zoologischer Garten Band 2, 23–29; Leipzig Akademische Verlagsgesellschaft MBH.

Moghe, M.A., 1951, 'Development and placentation of the Indian fruit bat (*Pteropus giganteus giganteus* Brunnich)'; *Proc. Zool. Soc. Lond.*, 121: 703–721.

Mohr, C.E., 1976, *The World of the Bat*; Living World Books, J.B. Lippincott Company, Philadelphia and New York.

Morrison, P.C., 1940, 'Are they extending? Along the track by the editor'; *Wild Life*, vol. 2, no. 5.

Morrison, P.C., 1943, 'Inland drive of the flying-fox: an interesting problem in habitat'; *Wild Life*, 5: 85–7.

Morton, P.A., 1992, 'Suggestions for long- and short-term education strategies to address the conservation of Pacific Island flying-foxes'; *Pacific Island Flying-foxes: Proceedings of an International Conservation Conference*, Eds Wilson, D.E. and Graham, G.L.; Biological Report 90(23).

Museum Godefroy, 1874, Catalog V. Nebst einer Beilage enthaltend topographische und zoologische Notizen; L. Friedrichsen & Co., Hamburg.

Musser, G.G., Koopman, K.F. & Califia, D., 1982, 'The Sulawesian *Pteropus arquatus* and *P. argentatus* are *Acerodon celebensis*; the Philippine *P. leucotis* is an *Acerodon*'; *J. Mammal.*, 63: 319–328.

Nelson, J.E., 1962, 'Flying-foxes'; *Australian Natural History*, vol. XIV, no. 1.

Nelson, J.E., 1963, 'The biology of the flying-fox (Genus *Pteropus*) in southeastern Queensland'; PhD Thesis, University of Queensland.

Nelson, J.E., 1964, 'Vocal communication in Australian flying-foxes (Pteropodidae; Megachiroptera); Zeitschrift fur Tierpsychologie, vol. 21, 7: 857–870.

Nelson, J.E., 1965a, 'Movements of Australian flying-foxes (Pteropodidae: Megachiroptera)'; *Aust. J. Zool.*, 13: 53–73.

Nelson, J.E., 1965b, 'Behaviour of Australian Pteropodidae (Megachiroptera)'; *Anim. Behav.*, 13: 544–557.

Neuweiler, G., 1962, Das Verhalten Indischer Flughunde (*Pteropus gigsanteus* gig. Brunn.) Die Naturwissenschaften; Heft 24.

Neuweiler, G., 1969, Verhaltensbeobachtungen an einer indischen Flughundkolonie; Zeitschrift fur Tierpsychologie, 26: 166–199.

Ogilby, J.D., 1892, *Catalogue of Australian Mammals with Introductory Notes on General Mammalogy*; Australian Museum, Sydney, catalogue no. 16.

Pallin, N., 1990, 'Contributions to bat conservation

by Ku-ring-gai bat colony committee inc.';
Australian Zoologist, vol. 26(2).

Parry-Jones, K.A., 'Winter flying-fox colonies in
Southern NSW'; *Australian Zoologist*, vol. 22, no. 2.

Parry-Jones, K., 1987, '*Pteropus poliocephalus*
(Chiroptera: Pteropodidae) in New South Wales';
Aust. Mammal., vol. 10, no. 2.

Parry-Jones, K. and Martin, L., 1987, 'Open forum
on movements and feeding patterns in flying-
foxes (Chiroptera: Pteropodidae)'; *Aust. Mammal.*,
vol. 10, no. 2.

Parry-Jones, K.A. and Augee, M.L., 1991, 'The diet
of flying-foxes in the Sydney and Gosford areas of
New South Wales, based on sighting reports
1986–1990'; *Australian Zoologist*, vol. 27 (3 & 4).

Parry-Jones, K.A. and Augee, M.L., 1992,
'Movements of grey-headed flying-foxes (*Pteropus
poliocephalus*) to and from a colony site on the
Central Coast of New South Wales'; *Wildlife
Research*, 19, 331–40.

Perez, G.S.A., 1968, 'Notes on Palau fruit bats';
J. Mammal., 49(4): 758.

Pettigrew, J.D. and Jamieson, B.G.M., 1987, 'Are
flying-foxes (Chiroptera: Pteropodidae) really
primates?'; *Aust. Mammal.*, vol. 10, no.2.

Pettigrew, J.D., 1991, 'Wings or brain? Convergent
evolution in the origins of bats'; *Systematic
Zoology*, vol. 40, 2: 199–216.

Pettigrew, J.D., 1991, 'A fruitful, wrong hypothesis?
Response to Baker, Novacek and Simmons';
Systematic Zoology, vol. 40, 2: 231–239.

Phua Poh Boon and Corlett, R.T., 1988, 'Seed
dispersal by the lesser short-nosed fruit bat
(*Cynopterus brachyotis*, Pteropodidae,
Megachiroptera)'; Department of Botany,
University of Hong Kong. Pokfulam Road, Hong
Kong.

Pierson, E.D. and Rainey, W.E., 1992, 'The biology
of flying-foxes of the genus *Pteropus*: a review';
*Pacific Island Flying-foxes: Proceedings of an
International Conservation Conference*, Eds Wilson,
D.E. & Graham G.L.; Biological Report 90(23).

Pizzey, G., 1963, 'Little red peril'; *Animals*,
2: 654–57.

Pook, G., 1978, 'Breeding the Rodrigues fruit bat
(*Pteropus rodricensis*) at the Jersey Zoological
Park'; *The Dodo*, 14: 30–33.

Prater, S.H., 1980, *Book of Indian Animals*; Bombay
Natural History Society.

Prociv, P., 1983, 'Seasonal Behaviour of *Pteropus
scapulatus* (Chiroptera: Pteropodidae)'; *Aust.
Mammalogy* 6: 45–46.

Raak, G., 1940, Allerlei aus unserem Zoologischen
Garten; Mitt. Zool. Garten Halle (Saale).

Racey, P., 1992, 'Flying-fox action plan'; *Pacific
Island Flying Foxes: Proceedings of an International
Conservation Conference*, Eds Wilson, D.E. and
Graham, G.L.; Biological Report 90(23).

Rainey, W.E. and Pierson, E.D., 1992, 'Distribution
of Pacific Island flying-foxes'; *Pacific Island Flying-
foxes: Proceedings of an International Conservation
Conference*, Eds Wilson, D.E. and Graham, G.L.;
Biological Report 90(23).

Ramsay, E.P., 1877–78, 'Zoology of the "Chevert",
Mammals, Part I; *Proc. Linn. Soc. NSW.*, vol. II.

Ramsay, E.P., 1878, 'Contributions to the zoology of
New Guinea Parts I & II'; *Proc. Linn. Soc. NSW.*,
vol. 3.

Ramsay, E.P., 1879, 'Contributions to the zoology of
New Guinea Parts IV & V'; *Proc. Linn. Soc. NSW.*,
vol. 4.

Ramsay, E.P., 1891, 'On a new species of Pteropine
bat from the New Britain Group'; *Records of the
Australian Museum*, vol. 1; Sydney, 1890–91.

Ratcliffe, F.N., 1931, 'The flying-fox (*Pteropus*) in
Australia'; *Commonwealth of Australia Council for
Scientific and Industrial Research Bulletin*, no. 53,
Melbourne.

Ratcliffe, F.N., 1947, *Flying Fox and Drifting Sand:
The Adventures of a Biologist in Australia*; Angus &
Robertson, Sydney, 1947.

Read, B.E., 1932, Chinese Materia Medica VI, Avian
Drugs; *Peking Natural History Bulletin*.

Reardon, T.B. and Flavel, S.C., 1987, *A Guide to the
Bats of South Australia*; South Australian Museum
in association with the Field Naturalists' Society
of South Australia (Inc.).

Richards, G.C. and Prociv, P., 1984, 'Folivory in
Pteropus'; *Australian Bat Research News*, 20.

Richards, G.C., 1987, 'Aspects of the ecology of
spectacled flying-foxes, *Pteropus conspicillatus*
(Chiroptera: Pteropodidae), in tropical
Queensland'; *Aust. Mammal.*, vol. 10, no. 2.

Richards, G.C., 1990, 'Rainforest bat conservation:
unique problems in a unique environment';
Australian Zoologist, vol. 26(2).

Richards, G.C., 1991, 'The conservation of forest
bats in Australia: do we really know the problems
and solutions?'; *Conservation of Australia's Forest
Fauna*, Ed. Lunney, D.; Royal Zoological Society
of NSW, Mosman.

Richardson, Sir John, Dallas, W.S., Cobbold, T.S.,
Baird, W. and White, A.; *The Museum of Natural
History with introductory essay on the Natural*

History of the Primeval World, vol. 1; William MacKenzie,London, Glasgow, Edinburgh.

Ride, W.D.L., 1970, *A Guide to the Native Mammals of Australia*; Oxford University Press, Melbourne.

Robertson, J., 1990, *The Complete Bat*; Chatto & Windus, London.

Robertson, P.B., 1992, 'Small islands, natural catastrophes, and rapidly disappearing forests: a high vulnerability recipe for island populations of flying-foxes'; *Pacific Island Flying-foxes: Proceedings of an International Conservation Conference*, Eds Wilson, D.E. and Graham, G.L.; Biological Report 90(23).

Robinson, N.H., 1985, 'Bats of the Illawarra region'; *Australian Zoologist*, vol. 22, no. 2.

Searcy, A., 1907, *In Australian Tropics*; Kegan Paul, Trench, Trubner & Co. Ltd, London.

Simmons, N.B., Novacek, M.J. & Baker, R.J., 1991, 'Approaches, methods, and the future of the chiropteran monophyly controversy: a reply to J.D. Pettigrew'; *Systematic Zoology*, vol. 40, 2: 239–243.

Sinavaiana, C. and Enright, J., 1992, 'The cultural significance of the flying-fox in Samoa: a legendary view'; *Pacific Island Flying-foxes: Proceedings of an International Conservation Conference*, Eds Wilson, D.E. and Graham, G.L.; Biological Report 90(23).

Smith, J.D., 1980, *Proc. 5th International Bat Research Conference*, Eds Wilson, D.E. and Gardner, A.L.; Texas Tech. Press, Lubbock.

Smith, J.D., 'Chiropteran phylogenetics: introduction'; *Proceedings, Fifth International Bat Research Conference*, Eds Wilson, D.E. and Gardner, A.L.; Texas Tech. Press, Lubbock.

Stager, K.E. and Hall, L.S., 1983, 'A cave-roosting colony of the black flying-fox (*Pteropus alecto*) in Queensland, Australia'; *J. Mamm.*, 64(3): 523–525.

Steller, D.C., 1986, 'The dietary energy and nitrogen requirements of the grey-headed flying-fox, *Pteropus poliocephalus* (Temminck) (Megachiroptera)'; *Aust. J. Zool.*, 34: 339–49.

Stephan, H. and Nelson, J.E., 1981, 'Brains of Australian chiroptera, I. encephalization and macromorphology; *Aust. J. Zool.*, 29: 653–70.

Stinson, D.W., Glass, P.O., and Estanislao, M.T., 1992, 'Declines and trade in fruit bats on Saipan, Tinian, Aguijan, and Rota'; *Pacific Island Flying-foxes: Proceedings of an International Conservation Conference*, Eds Wilson, D.E. and Graham. G.L.; Biological Report 90(23).

Strahan, R., Ed., 1983; *The Australian Museum Complete Book of Australian Mammals*; Angus & Robertson, Sydney.

Strahan, R., 1981, *A Dictionary of Australian Mammal Names*; Angus & Robertson, Sydney.

Strum, S., 1987, *Almost Human: A Journey into the World of Baboons*; Elm Tree Books, London.

Suthers, R.A., 1970, 'Vision, olfaction, taste', in Wimsatt, W.A., Ed., *Biology of Bats*, vol. II; Academic Press, New York and London.

Tate, G.H.H., 1942, 'Results of the Archbold expeditions, no. 48, Pteropodidae (Chiroptera) of the Archbold collections; *Bull. Amer. Mus. Nat. Hist.*, vol. 80, 331–347.

Tate, G.H.H., 1952, 'Results of the Archbold expeditions, no. 66, Mammals of Cape York Peninsula, with notes on the occurrence of rainforest in Queensland; *Bull. Am. Mus. Nat. Hist.*, vol. 98, art. 7.

Tedman, R.A. and Hall, L.S., 1985, The morphology of the gastro-intestinal tract and food transit time in the fruit bats *Pteropus alecto* and *P. poliocephalus*; *Aust. J. Zool.* 33: 625–640.

Tennent, Sir J. Emerson, 1861, *Sketches of the Natural History of Ceylon with narratives and anecdotes illustrative of the Habits and Instincts of the Mammalia, Birds, Reptiles, Fishes Insects &c. Including a monograph of the Elephant and a description of the modes of capturing and training it*; Longman, Green, Longman, & Roberts, London.

Temminck, C.J., 1827, Monographies de Mammalogie, ou descriptions de quelques genres de mammiferes, dont les especes ont ete observees dans les differens musees de l'Europe; G. Dufour et Ed, D'oCagne, Paris.

Thomas, O., 1882, 'Description of two new species of *Pteropus* from the Caroline Islands'; *Proc. Zool. Soc. Lond.*

Thomas, O., 1887, 'Diagnoses of two new fruit-eating bats from the Solomon Islands'; *Ann. Mag. Nat. Hist.*, vol. XIX, 5th series.

Thomas, O., 1894, 'Diagnosis of a new *Pteropus* from the Admiralty Islands'; *Ann. Mag. Nat. Hist.*, ser. 6, vol. 13, p. 293.

Thomas, O., 1904, 'New species of *Pteropus, Mus* and *Pogonomys* from the Australian region'; *Novitates Zool.*, vol. 11, 597–600.

Tideman, C.R., 1987, 'Notes on the flying-fox *Pteropus melanotus* (Chiroptera: Pteropodidae), on Christmas Island, Indian Ocean'; *Aust. Mammal.*, vol. 10, no. 2.

Tideman, C.R. and Nelson, J.E., 1987, 'Flying-foxes (Chiroptera: Pteropodidae) and bananas:

some interactions'; *Aust. Mammal.*, vol. 10, no. 2.

Tiraa, A., 1992, 'The Moa Kirikiri of the Cook Islands'; *Pacific Island Flying-foxes: Proceedings of an International Conservation Conference*, Eds Wilson, D.E. and Graham, G.L.; Biological Report 90(23).

Tomes, R.F., 1858, 'Notice of five species of bats in the collection of L.L. Dillwyn, Esq., M.P; collected in Labuan by Mr. James Motley'; *Proc. Zool. Soc. London.*

Trenerry, M., 1992, *Summary of the Mammals, Reptiles and Amphibians of the Cairns Central Swamp;* North Queensland Naturalists Club, edition no. 194.

Troughton, E. Le G., 1926–1927, 'Fixation of the habitat, and extended description, of *Pteropus tuberculatus*, Peters'; *Records of the Australian Museum*, vol. XV, Sydney.

Troughton, E. Le G., 1929, 'A new fruit bat (*Pteropus rayneri* group) from the Solomons'; *Rec. Australian Museum*, 17.4: 193–198.

Troughton, E. Le G., 1933–1936, 'The mammalian fauna of Bougainville Island, Solomons Group'; *Records of the Australian Museum*, vol. XIX.

Troughton, E. Le G., 1930, 'A new species and subspecies of fruit bats (*Pteropus*) from the Santa Cruz group'; Ibid., vol. 18, 1–4.

Troughton, E. Le G., 1931, 'Three new bats of the genera *Pteropus, Nyctimene* and *Chaerephon* from Melanesia'; *Proc. Linn. Soc. N.S.W.*, vol. LVI.

Troughton, E. Le G., 1967, *Furred Animals of Australia*, 9th edn; Angus & Robertson, Sydney.

Van Deusen, H.M., 1969, '5. A new species of *Pteropus* (Mammalia, Pteropodidae) from New Britain, Bismark Archipelago, Results of the 1958–1959 Gilliard New Britain Expedition; *American Museum Novitates*, no. 2371.

Wallace, A.R., 1869, *The Malay Archipelago: the land of the Orang-Utan, and the Bird of Paradise*, vol. II; Macmillan & Co., London.

West C.C. and Redshaw, M.E., 1987, 'Maternal behaviour in the Rodrigues fruit bat'; *The Dodo*, Jersey Wildl. Pres. Trust, no. 24.

Whewell, G.D., 1992, 'Flying-foxes in the Solomon Islands'; *Pacific Island Flying-foxes: Proceedings of an International Conservation Conference*, Eds Wilson, D.E. and Graham, G.L.; Biological Report 90(23).

Whitmee, Rev. S.J., 1874, *Letter in Proc. Zool. Soc. London.*, 666–667.

Wiles, G.J., 1987, 'Current research and future management of Mariannus fruit bats (Chiroptera: Pteropodidae) on Guam'; *Aust. Mammal.*, vol. 10, no. 2.

Wiles G.J. and Fujita, M.S., 1992, 'Food plants and economic importance of flying-foxes on Pacific Islands'; *Pacific Island Flying-foxes: Proceedings of an International Conservation Conference*, Eds Wilson, D.E. and Graham, G.L.; Biological Report 90(23).

Wiles, G.J., 1992, 'Recent trends in the fruit bat trade on Guam'; *Pacific Island Flying-foxes: Proceedings of an International Conservation Conference*, Eds Wilson, D.E. and Graham G.L.; Biological Report 90(23).

Williams, R. and George, H., 1983, 'Hand-rearing grey-headed fruit bats and observations on the growth of captive bred animals'; *Proc. 4th Ann. Conf. Australasian Society of Zoo Keepers.*

Wilson, D.E. and GRAHAM, G.L., Eds, 1992, *Pacific Island Flying Foxes: Proceedings of an International Conservation Conference, Biological Report* 90(23); U.S. Department of the Interior Fish and Wildlife Service, Washington DC, 20240.

Wilson, D.E. and Engbring, J., 1992, 'The flying-foxes *Pteropus samoensis* and *Pteropus tonganus*: status in Fiji and Samoa'; *Pacific Island Flying-foxes: Proceedings of an International Conservation Conference*, Eds Wilson, D.E. and Graham, G.L.; Biological Report 90(23).

Wimsatt, W.A., Ed., 1970, 1977, *Biology of Bats*, I, II, III; Academic Press, New York.

Wood, J.G., *The Illustrated Natural History, vol. I. Mammalia;* Routledge, Warne & Routledge, London.

Young, J.A., 1987, 'A note on the hand-rearing and reintegration of an infant Rodrigues fruit bat'; *The Dodo*, Jersey Wildl. Pres. Trust, no. 24.

Young, J.A. and Carroll, J.B., 1989, 'Male-female associations in captive Rodrigues fruit bats, *Pteropus rodricensis'; The Dodo,* Jersey Wildl. Pres. Trust, no. 26.

Young, J., 1993, 'World's rarest fruit bat comes to Jersey'; *On the Edge*, no. 66; Jersey Wildlife Presrvation Trust.

Zoological Society of London, 1896, *List of the Vertebrated Animals now or Lately Living in the Gardens of the Zoological Society of London*, 9th edn; Longmans, Green & Co., London.

Zubaid, A. and Fatimah, A.M., 1990, 'Hair morphology of Malaysian Pteropodids'; *Mammalia*, 54 (4): 627–632

DATE DUE

599.774
Con

AUTHOR Conder, Pamela

TITLE With Wings on Their
Fingers, An Intimate
DATE DUE View of the Flying Fox BORROWER'S NAME